ART NOUVEAU DESIGNS
FROM THE SILVER STUDIO COLLECTION
1885 – 1910

Eton planted

ART NOUVEAU DESIGNS
FROM THE SILVER STUDIO COLLECTION
1885 – 1910

by Mark Turner
with
Lesley Hoskins
Juliet Kinchin
and
William Ruddick

Middlesex Polytechnic London

Dedication

This exhibition is dedicated to the memory of Margaret Stoll who, after retiring from Middlesex Polytechnic, worked voluntarily at the Silver Studio Collection cataloguing and indexing designs until her death in 1984.

© Middlesex Polytechnic

This is the official catalogue for the exhibition, Art Nouveau Designs from the Silver Studio Collection 1885–1910, held at the Hunterian Art Gallery, University of Glasgow, from 7 February 1986 to 27 March 1986.

Cover illustration: Cat No 22
Title page illustration: Cat No 149
ISBN 0 904804 51 8

Designed by Elaine Bradley
Edited by Roberta de Joia

Published by Middlesex Polytechnic
Chase Side, London N14
Printed and bound by Office Services
Middlesex Polytechnic

Contents

Acknowledgements

Our very greatest thanks are due to Miss Mary Peerless (Rex Silver's step-daughter) whose foresight in ensuring that the archives of the Silver Studio went to a public institution has earned her the gratitude of all who care about the history of British decorative design.

We have long wanted to mount an exhibition devoted to Silver Studio Art Nouveau and we are very grateful to the Hunterian Art Gallery for giving us the opportunity of doing so. In particular we would like to thank Mrs Pamela Robertson for all her support and kindness. We have included a section in the catalogue on the Glasgow manufacturers that bought Silver Studio designs in the late nineteenth century. Miss Juliet Kinchin and Mrs Elizabeth Arthur of Glasgow Museums and Art Galleries very kindly wrote histories of these manufacturers and we are most grateful for this.

Lesley Hoskins, research assistant for the Silver Studio Collection, and William Ruddick, lecturer in English literature at Manchester University, have both contributed thoughtful and scholarly articles on the Art Nouveau Interior Decoration and Silver Studio Art Nouveau respectively.

Special thanks are due to Mrs William Haxworth and Mrs Herman Silver who have very kindly lent silver designed for Liberty by their father, Harry Silver.

As with all our exhibitions, the bulk of the work has fallen on the Silver Studio's two conservators, Sarah Mansell and June Marshall. Without their tireless efforts this exhibition would have been impossible.

We are totally dependent at the Silver Studio Collection on the magnificent efforts of our volunteer assistants. It would not have been possible to mount this exhibition without them and we cannot thank them enough for their loyalty and hard work. From the Harrow National Association of Decorative and Fine Art Societies are Mrs Ann Murray, Mrs Denise Tucker and Mrs Ethel Tucker, who have all helped Sarah Mansell with paper conservation. Also from Harrow are Mrs Diane Clipson, Mrs Janet Phillips, Mrs Muriel Rata and Mrs Mavis Starns who have helped June Marshall with textile conservation. Mrs Elizabeth Baxter has been of invaluable help in both fields. From Highgate National Association of Decorative and Fine Art Societies are Mrs Ann Pollack and Mrs Rachel Dulley, who have been working on the conservation of textiles. Two former members of Middlesex Polytechnic staff, Mrs Frances Rackley and Mrs Peggy Fincken, have worked incredibly hard on typing the manuscript of this catalogue as well as doing much cataloguing and indexing of the collection. Mrs Rackley has had special responsibility for the books and journals in the collection and Mrs Fincken has worked largely on recording the designs. Mrs Sheila Levy has been continually involved with the collection since 1978 and has worked tirelessly for sales of catalogues, cards and tapestries and has done much cataloguing for the collection. Mrs Thelma Riley, a postgraduate student of the Polytechnic, has also given us superb cataloguing assistance.

We have been very fortunate in having a volunteer research assistant, Julia Wheal, who has helped with the preparation of this catalogue as well as cataloguing the textiles in the collection.

We are very grateful to Mr Philip Jeffreys for his superb photography for this catalogue and for the collection as a whole.

Within Middlesex Polytechnic, we have received the greatest help and support with this exhibition from Mr David Cheshire and Mrs Bobby de Joia, who have always done all they could to help the Silver Studio Collection. The production of this catalogue owes much to the help and expertise of the Polytechnic's Office Services and Information Centre.

Finally, we owe special thanks to Elaine Bradley who not only has worked as a volunteer on the photographic archive at the Silver Studio Collection, but has designed this catalogue with great skill and artistry.

The Silver Studio Steering Committee
Middlesex Polytechnic
Bounds Green Road
London N11 2NQ
January 1986

Introduction

This exhibition examines the very important contribution made by the Silver Studio to the development of British Art Nouveau.

The Silver Studio was started by Arthur Silver in West London in 1880 and rapidly became Britain's largest design studio, supplying designs principally for wallpapers, furnishing textiles, carpets, linoleum and metalwork. It was easily the greatest source of Art Nouveau designs for commercial manufacture in this country and as a consequence its influence was very great indeed. During the period 1885 to 1910 the Silver Studio sold literally thousands of designs in a style which we would now call Art Nouveau. Furthermore, these designs were sold not just in Britain but in Europe and the United States. An even more important factor in the spread of Silver Studio design influence abroad was the flourishing export of wallpapers and textiles by British manufacturers to American and European department stores. Thus it was easily possible in the early years of this century to buy Silver Studio designed wallpapers and textiles as far apart as Chicago and Vienna.

Interestingly, the Silver Studio never described its designs as Art Nouveau. This was a term which was usually applied only to the most exaggerated decorative designs of the French or other European countries (and, of course, Charles Rennie Macintosh and his colleagues in Glasgow). Art Nouveau was felt to be decadent, fin-de-siecle and very un-British. Instead, adjectives such as 'quaint', 'modern', or 'flat' were used to describe designs and objects which featured such characteristic motifs as sinuous stylised flowers and lush, organic curving leaves — in particular 'quaint' was used to describe British Art Nouveau and became as universal a description of modern design as 'artistic' in the 1880s, 'modernist' in the 1930s and 'contemporary' in the 1950s.

The 1880s, when Arthur Silver's studio was establised, was a decade of revolution in attitudes to home decoration and furnishing. For the first time in British history a large percentage of the population was taking a serious interest in the aesthetics of interior decoration. Previously, interior decoration was the prerogative of the very rich, but during the 1870s and 80s the actual cost of most household goods was falling at a time when middle class earnings were rising. At the same time, the British government had established schools of art in most large towns to raise the nation's standard of art education and design consciousness. (Arthur Silver had attended his local school of art in Reading). The effect of the excellent training of these schools was making itself felt in a rapid rise in standards of pattern and three dimensional design.

Prior to the 1880s most British people were very restricted in their options for home decoration. Not only was their choice of wallpapers, carpets, furniture and textiles very limited, but the cost, in proportion to income, was extremely high. Writers on home decoration in the 1880s, such as Colonel Edis and

Mrs Panton, recalled with loathing the 1850s and 60s and wrote of the difficulties faced by young middle class couples trying to set up home. They complained of massive and ugly furniture, extremely dull colour ranges and, above all, high prices. There is also plenty of evidence to suggest that there was little interest shown in home decoration in the mid nineteenth century. Mrs Panton wrote of how middle class families preferred to spend large sums of money on food and drink and never thought to replace curtains or carpets, which in any case were chosen more for their ability to last than for any aesthetic considerations. There can be no doubt that the rapid increase in prosperity of the urban middle class in the late nineteenth century was responsible for the phenomenal growth of interest in interior decoration. To the lasting benefit of designers and manufacturers alike, it became smart to take an interest in all aspects of decoration.

As a writer in *The Builder* remarked in 1877 "..... indifference to the aesthetics of home furniture and decoration can hardly be openly professed by any who have the hope of social salvation." In the 1860s good middle class housewives cared far more about keeping fleas out of their feather beds than the aesthetics of wallpaper patterns, and as a contemporary upholsterer remarked, "would as soon have weighed a chair as consider its style." Increased prosperity meant more domestic help. (A lower-middle-class salary of £100 in the 1880s enabled the keeping of a general servant and a char for 'the rough'). More domestic help meant more leisure in which to visit the new department stores. It also meant time to read magazines and so learn about the beauties of Japanese art or the delightful wallpaper patterns of Mr William Morris. No longer was the middle class housewife occupied with brewing and baking or the still-room duties of making cordials and preparing simple medicines. With the house safely in the hands of efficient servants, she could visit Liberty, Whitely's, Waring and Gillow, or Wylie and Lochead's.

The development of British Art Nouveau went hand-in-hand with the growing prosperity and gradual emancipation of the middle class housewife. Interior decoration was one of the few outlets she had for self expression and in this she was abetted, from the 1880s onwards, by many books on the decoration of the home — mostly written by women of a similar background.

Given this degree of interest it is hardly surprising that the leading designers and manufacturers of the day became household names. Manufacturers such as Woollams, Sanderson, Jeffrey & Co, and Templetons all found it paid to use the best designers of the day and to advertise the fact. The young Arthur Silver could hardly have chosen a better decade than the 1880s in which to launch his studio of design.

Arthur Silver was born in Reading in 1853. His father, James, was a prosperous shopkeeper of the old school. His business was primarily that of upholsterer, but like most country town upholsterers, his business extended to cover every aspect of buying and furnishing a home. James would undertake to find a customer a house and arrange insurance as well as providing all furniture and furnishings. It was an ideal background for a designer, as Arthur would have been familiar with every conceivable type of furnishing textile and carpet and it partly explains why he so readily understood the practical aspects of designing.

He attended Reading School of Art from 1869 to 1872 and then went up to London as an apprentice of the then famous Henry Batley. Batley was an Aesthetic designer *par excellence*. Although he specialised in designing for furniture he was also particularly good at carpet designs, and it was the training that Arthur received in this difficult area of designing that enabled him to do such excellent work for Templeton's of Glasgow. Batley was particularly fond of Japanese Art and used motifs from Japanese prints in many of his designs both for furniture and textiles. It is certain that he first introduced Arthur to this source for so much of Silver Studio Art Nouveau. It is likely, too, that Arthur Silver first became familiar with the work of William Morris and Christopher Dresser whilst still an apprentice.

It was in 1880 that Arthur decided to open his own studio of design. It was exactly one year after his marriage to Isabella Walenn, whose own family were also artistically very gifted. As I mentioned earlier, the timing was extremely propitious. By 1880 there was great interest in all aspects of house decoration, and William Morris textiles in particular were very popular and sought after. Arthur Silver, like all the best late nineteenth century designers, was no stranger to William Morris's source of designs, the Victoria and Albert Museum. It was an easy matter for him to produce designs based on the sixteenth and seventeenth century embroideries and tapestries which had formed the source for so many Morris papers and chintzes. The flat, decorative treatment of flowers and leaves, in particular large heavy flowers such as chrysanthemums, and vigorous scrolling leaves such as those of the acanthus, became a major basis for the development of Art Nouveau. Manufacturers such as John Line (whose father had been a Reading friend of Arthur's father, James) quickly started to buy as many of these designs as Arthur could produce. Catalogue numbers 10 and 17 are typical of these.

Japanese goods and prints had only been available in Britain since the 1860s and in the 1880s the Japanese craze was still very much at its height. The demand for Japanese inspired patterns was, as a consequence, very great and Arthur Silver lost no time in providing these (see catalogue numbers 13 and 26), and so began the biggest influence on the development of Art Nouveau. Arthur subscribed to Bing's *Artistic Japan* from 1889 onwards to maintain a constant supply of reproductions of Japanese prints. Also in 1889 he started to exhibit at the annual Arts and Crafts Exhibitions, which helped not only to establish the Silver Studio as a major source of avant-garde patterns, but also enabled him to make many useful contacts with other manufacturers and designers.

Silver Studio Art Nouveau really begins in the early 1890s when the results of a careful observation of historic textiles in the Victoria and Albert Museum are combined with elements from Japanese art. A typical design is *The Floral Sea* of 1890, and is a perfect example of the type of design that established Arthur Silver's reputation as a leading designer of the day. It is, of course, largely Japanese in inspiration but there is a strong Morris/Mackmurdo influence in the incorporation of curves of stylised flowers. It was manufactured as a chintz, and illustrated in *The Studio* magazine in 1894. We know exactly the historic textiles that Arthur Silver was looking at as in 1889 he launched a very successful series of photographs of textiles, known as *The Silvern Series,* in the Victoria and Albert Museum. They were sold to both designers and manufacturers alike (see catalogue number 15). In about 1890 Arthur Silver was particularly fortunate in employing two extremely able young designers, John Illingworth Kay and Harry Napper. Both seem to have had highly developed Art Nouveau styles from the early 1890s (see catalogue numbers 90 and 105).

John Illingworth Kay's designs are characterised by a strong Japanese landscape quality. His stylised trees and flowers are often set in pseudo Oriental landscapes with topographical features such as streams and hills. Napper's designs are far more Western in origin, and can be seen to be a continuation of the work of William Morris. It is also apparent that his work owes a great deal to Aubrey Beardsley whose illustrations were frequently in *The Studio* magazine in the 1890s. Napper's flowers are often given a very flat treatment, almost like plates, whilst leaves have sharp, jagged edges. A great tragedy is that although the Silver Studio's records have survived intact to a degree that is little short of miraculous, there is almost nothing on the designers who were working with Arthur in the 1890s. It is difficult, too, to attribute designers on a stylistic basis as there was such an intermingling of visual ideas and styles in the 1890s through journals such as *The Studio* and the Arts and Crafts Exhibitions.

By the time of Arthur Silver's wretchedly premature death in 1896, the Silver Studio was established as the most important commercial design studio in Britain. Arthur's name was consistently linked with designers such as Walter Crane, Lewis F Day, Christopher Dresser and CFA Voysey, all of whom he knew very well indeed. As his son Rex was too young to take over the running of the studio, the management was handed to Harry Napper for two years and subsequently JR Houghton. Rex Silver took over the studio management in 1901, with his younger brother Harry as design manager.

Under Harry Napper's management, the Silver Studio produced nothing but magnificent Art Nouveau designs for an enormous range of manufacturers. As the designs became increasingly stylised, so the colours began to change, too. Until the late 1890s, most of the designs were in secondary and tertiary colours — sage green, terracotta, subtle mixtures of blues and greens. These were the colours that first became popular in the 1880s and were referred to jokingly as 'greenery-yallery'. They are perhaps best seen in Arthur Silver's very successful stencilling venture with Alexander Rottmann in 1895. It is obvious that Harry Napper's own preference was for much stronger, clearer colours, and so designs began to be done in rich reds, greens and blues (see catalogue numbers 110 and 133). Although Liberty and other English manufacturers still demand sage green and ochres, European manufacturers wanted more demonstrative colours. The demand in Europe (particularly France and Belgium) for Silver Studio Art Nouveau began to grow in the early 1890s. It was chiefly in north-eastern France that the Silver Studio sold designs to the big manufacturers of machine woven textiles such as Leborgne and Vanoutryve (see catalogue numbers 141, 142 and 143). By 1901 when Rex Silver took over his father's studio, at least 50 per cent of studio work went to Europe and America and we must not forget the vast sales of English manufactured goods from Silver Studio designs when assessing the Silver Studio's influence on Continental Art Nouveau.

It seems almost certain that Harry Napper was instrumental in arranging for the Silver Studio to supply designs from 1898 onwards to Liberty for their new range of Cymric silver, and subsequently Tudric pewter. It was devised as a scheme to produce a cheaper version of Ashbee's Guild of Handicraft metalwork (see catalogue number 115), and was immensely successful. It seems that we shall never be certain who was responsible within the studio for the production of the wonderfully elegant Celtic designs which epitomise the best of English Art Nouveau. Undoubtedly some are by Archibald Knox who knew Rex Silver through Christopher Dresser and who undoubtedly worked for or at the Silver Studio, as his name occurs on an old Silver Studio inventory of 1933. Many of the designs have Isle of Man place names (see catalogue number 117). As this was Knox's birthplace, it can safely be assumed these are by him. Others have such detailed working notes in Rex Silver's hand that it seems unthinkable that they are not at least partly by him.

In my catalogue, *A London Design Studio 1880—1963,* I suggested that Rex Silver's involvement with the production of these important designs was limited to administration. I now feel sure he was responsible in part for the execution of some. The old arguments against this, however, still apply. It is hard to understand why these early metalwork designs were never photographed for the Silver Studio records. One of the greatest joys of the Silver Studio Collection is the almost complete photographic record of all sold designs form 1889 until 1963. All the later metalwork (from 1904 to 1910) by Harry Silver was photographed. If Rex was wholly responsible for some or all of the early designs, it seems very curious that there is no photographic record. Many different styles can be called Art Nouveau and a glance at a copy of *The Studio* magazine for the late 1890s will show how easily the works of designers can be emulated. The more stylised a design the easier it is to copy. With such a dearth of evidence it is very hard to prove conclusive authorship of many of the earlier metalwork sketches in the collection.

However, there is no doubt that Knox introduced Celtic art to the Silver Studio and this was to have a significant influence on their later Art Nouveau designs. The work of Arts and Crafts architects and designers such as Voysey, Ashbee and Baillie Scott were also having a profound influence on the commercial production of Art Nouveau textiles and wallpapers. The great emphasis they placed on wholesome, light, cottagey domestic architecture and design was quickly taken up by the studio. Smart manufacturers were still anxious that their products reflected avant-garde taste and this meant designs that were light, simple and in clear colours. (See catalogue number 162). Reproductions of William Morris chintzes still provided much of the studio's bread-and-butter work and Harry Silver specialised in these.

As the 1900s progressed, Continental Art Nouveau became increasingly formalised and abstracted but in England there were signs that as a decorative style, it was declining in popularity. In the photographic records kept by the Silver Studio we can clearly see how their Art Nouveau designs (particularly those done for export to Europe) increased in stylisation during the 1900s. At the same time we can observe that Rex and Harry were producing designs which were accurate reproductions of historic textiles. (See catalogue numbers 170 and 172). The nearer to 1910, the greater the number. Rex and Harry had been trained by their father to produce designs in a wide variety of historic styles. This was just as well, for by 1910 the English middle classes had completely abandoned Art Nouveau in favour of furnishings which would complement the growing craze for antique furniture. During the years surrounding the First World War Harry Silver and Winifred Mold did some enchanting simple modern designs (known as Futurist) for Foxton's but these were a tiny proportion of the studio's output. Art Nouveau had become just another out-of-date style. Emmulating the great decorating style of British history had become the fashion which was to last well into the 1930s.

Mark Turner

Interior Decoration and Art Nouveau

British Art Nouveau was an attempt to find a new national style, a style for the modern age. But like all new decorative styles it made use of already existing ideas and conventions. Its immediate fashionable predecessor, 'aesthetic' decoration, was both a foil and an inspiration. At the same time, the development of Art Nouveau was so closely associated with the Arts and Crafts Movement that it can sometimes be difficult to distinguish the two. With its complicated parentage, Art Nouveau did not spring up overnight, but beginning in the 1880s, reached the peak of its popularity in the early 1900s.

In the nineteenth century, and especially in its last quarter, more people than ever before were interested in the decorative arts and interior decoration. Increasingly mechanised production, cheap imports of raw materials and finished goods, changes in finance and commerce, improvements in transport and the development of shops and department stores not only played their part in making a wide range of cheaper goods readily available, but also required an enlarged white-collar class to service these changes. Of this middle class, a few were very rich, some were substantially prosperous, but the majority were fairly lowly paid. Clerks, for example, might earn only £100 a year. However, even they, in secure employment and with shorter working hours, had enough money to buy, and leisure to enjoy, the new domestic goods.

'The home' was an important centre of family, social and even moral life for the Victorian middle classes and it is not surprising that much of their surplus time and money went into the decoration of their houses. But *how* were they to decorate? How were they to choose between the great variety of styles available in furniture, wallpaper, textiles and all the other necessities of domestic adornment?

Previously the upholsterer had been the person to help, providing not just the covers and curtains but whole decorative schemes. However, with department stores and furniture show rooms, such as Whitely's 'The Universal Provider', displaying domestic items of every kind and with pattern books and catalogues, individuals were able to make their own decisions. Fortunately they were not left unaided as more and more books and articles appeared giving advice. There were already household handbooks, such as the 1857 *Walshes Manual of Domestic Economy,* but these were concerned with domestic management as a whole and considered the durability of furnishings more important than their appearance. At a time when the purchase of a table or set of curtains was a very considerable expense[1] it is not surprising that serviceability was the major concern. The advent of cheaper goods changed this.

What was new about books like Charles Eastlake's *Hints on Household Taste* (1872) and the *Art in the Home* series (1876—8) was that they concerned themselves as much with style and taste as with function. They were directed at the new prosperous

1 JH Walsh, *A Manual of Domestic Economy* 1857. See pp192—212 for list of furniture prices.

middle classes with an income of about £500 to £1,000 per annum, who while they might have money, were seen as lacking the inherited 'good taste' of the upper classes. They needed to be educated, for left to themselves they were attracted to the cheap and showy, to factory made approximations of upper class fashions. These new books could be immensely detailed. Mrs Panton, a most successful and prolific writer, was even willing to make suggestions about the front gate. One of the most important requirements was that decoration should be 'artistic', a term often used but not clearly defined. Artistic surroundings not only proclaimed the sensibility of their owner, they provided a standard of beauty which could be morally and spiritually uplifting.

That ordinary domestic objects could be beautiful and should be well made was an important idea that had been gaining strength throughout the nineteenth century. It was a motivation to numbers of attempts to improve the standard of industrially manufactured goods as well as being one of the inspirations of the Arts and Crafts Movement. With William Morris as their best known proponent, from the 1860s onwards a number of idealistic groups and individuals were working to produce handmade decorative art embodying the principle of truth to materials and the value of honest labour. Although craftsman made goods were far too expensive for most people to buy, and although the Arts and Crafts Movement was, at least in its early years, opposed to industrial manufacture on the grounds that it demeaned both workmen and goods, its ideals and stylistic principles were immensely influential, even on mass production. And by 1880, when Arthur Silver set up his own design studio, there was a keen and widespread interest in the decorative arts.

At this time fashionable upper class taste tended to the French, to the styles of Louis XV and XVI, while factory made approximations of these and English Renaissance forms, rich with ornate machine carving and elaborate upholstery, were popular at the lower end of the market. Social conventions divided up the middle class house: servants and children were kept as separate as space allowed and other rooms were considered to be predominantly male or female domains and were decorated accordingly. The drawing-room could be in a light and pretty French style while something heavier, darker and more masculine, such as Jacobean or Queen Anne, was considered appropriate for the dining-room and library. Advanced 'artistic' taste, however, in the 1870s and 80s favoured the 'Aesthetic' method of decoration which brought exotic elements — Japanese art, peacock feathers, bamboo furniture and Mooresque arches — into these conventions.

In 1889 *Woman's World* (edited by Oscar Wilde) described the drawing-room of the sort of young lady likely to be found shopping at Liberty, the aesthete's Mecca:

> 'We may be tolerably certain that such a one has her drawing- room arranged in the very latest scheme of

2 These colours occur with great frequency in the work of the Silver Studio from 1885 up to 1900.

3 *The Woman's World,* Vol 1889, p6.

4 *Anaglypta* Catalogue of circa 1890, Catalogue number 18 with examples by Arthur Silver for dado papers and friezes.

colour — cool silver-grey, possibly, in conjunction with yellow, terracotta and ivory or the new red-brown with the faintest, palest of olive-greens[2]. The floor in parqueterie with rich Eastern rugs laid down on it, tiny tables, yellow, white or pale green; graceful palms in huge pots of Eastern pottery in beaten iron stands; a fretwork arch in wood dividing the double rooms. Imagination further conjures up the lady herself in a tea-gown of silver-grey pongee cashmere, with full front of yellow surah..... So we leave her, deep in discussion with her friend and the Eastern garmented shop-girl as to the relative merits of a sage green or dull red portière[3]...'

This rather tongue-in-cheek description shows aestheticism in an extreme form but popular writers like Mrs Panton and Colonel Robert Edis adapted it for more general use.

A very widespread convention was the division of the wall into different areas — skirting, dado to a height of about three and a half feet, filling and frieze, which ran under the cornice to a depth of eighteen inches to two feet. The dado was covered with some tough material such as Japanese embossed paper or anaglypta[4], and the filling was papered with a highly conventionalised pattern. Although aesthetic movement colours were often quite pale, darker tertiary shades also had a vogue. Mrs Panton was very fond of deep shades of blue-electric turquoise and hedge-sparrow's egg tint for example. Generally, the colours became lighter towards the ceiling; the floor, with Oriental or Turkey carpets on a painted and varnished wood surround was the darkest area. The paint of the woodwork followed one of the darker colours of the wall or might even be black. There was a great deal of rich, highly finished pattern in these rooms. The mouldings of the woodwork and the raised surfaces on the dadoes and friezes were picked out in different shades or gilded, while flat friezes and door panels could be stencilled or decorated with paintings. For this, and for the wall filling, Japanese influenced flower or bird motifs were extremely popular. The fireplace remained the main feature of the room.

Although great gilded and mirrored overmantels were no longer fashionable, their replacements in plain or painted wood were very tall, with numerous shelves and brackets for the display of flowers, peacocks' feathers, Japanese fans, china, photographs and a clock. The fireplace could be further dressed with a frill around the mantelshelf and curtains in front of the grate, opened enough to reveal a Japanese umbrella. Shelves around the dado or frieze and brackets over the door displayed yet more blue and white china. With both lace and heavy curtains at the windows, draped portières in front of the doors, covers on the tables, a substantial amount of furniture and innumerable artistic knick-knacks, such rooms were very full and dark by modern standards although they must have looked marvellous by lamplight.

These cluttered rooms were recommended even in the face of the Victorian middle class belief that dust and dirt carried disease. Although Venetian and Holland blinds were disappearing, allowing more light and air into the rooms, and carpet squares which could be taken up and shaken were preferred to fitted carpets, cleanliness, in the living rooms at least, was obtained more by hard work than by simplification. It was mainly in the bedrooms that decorative concessions were made to hygiene. Wall and window decorations were reduced for ease of cleaning; stuffy, dusty bed canopies and draperies were removed; metal bedsteads which, unlike wood, were not thought to harbour germs were recommended. This kind of decoration continued to be popular well into the 1880s but, with the emotional intensity of aestheticism ridiculed, for example in *Punch* and in Gilbert and Sullivan's comic opera *Patience,* and with 'Art' furnishings widely and cheaply available, it was seen to have become vulgarised and 'advanced taste' moved on. The 'modern', 'quaint', 'New Art' and 'New Renaissance' styles (as Art Nouveau was variously known in Britain) of the 1880s to 1900s were partly a reaction against the aesthetic craze although they did, in fact, employ some of its features.

HJ Jennings wrote in 1902:

> 'Gone is the so-called "Aesthetic Movement" with all its fantastic folly. Its affectations no longer flourish. Its once popular drawing-rooms, with their peacocks's feathers and Japanese tea trays no longer exist. Blue and white teapots are no longer "intense"; the gospel of the "Too, too" falls no more on receptive ears; society has forsworn the creed that "The incongruous is the expression of the Utter". But it must in fairness be admitted that the Aesthetic Movement, of which this craze was but the rank growth, sowed precious seed. People began to realise that it was possible to make their homes more beautiful. William Morris, Walter Crane and other great designers devoted their skill to the improvement of decorative art. The Century Guild led the way in an appreciation of the best examples of eighteenth century English furniture.'[5]

5 HJ Jennings, *Our Homes and How to Beautify Them,* 1902, pp55—56.

Morris's idealisation of medieval craftsmanship and forms was certainly very important but there were other crucial influences in the development of the New Art, perhaps the most significant of which was Japanese art. The opening up of Japan to Western trade in 1858 had not only provided the aesthetic with knick-knacks, it proved a serious source of inspiration for designers like Christopher Dresser, Arthur Silver and EW Godwin, whose influential work echoed the structural simplicity of Japanese art. Arthur Heygate Mackmurdo, also influenced by Japan, was particularly important in the evolution of Art Nouveau. His printed textiles and graphic work, from as early as 1882, showed the rhythmic, linear conventionalisation of natural forms that was typical of British Art Nouveau two dimensional and low relief work. Mackmurdo founded The Century Guild in 1882. This, like other Arts and Crafts guilds of around the same time, was a group of designers and craftsmen producing furniture and decorative art of all kinds but it also produced a journal, *The Hobby Horse,* promoting Arts and Crafts ideals. Although short-lived, this was part of the Movement's increasing visibility which contributed to The New Art becoming a popular fashionable style. The efforts of The Arts and Crafts Exhibition Society from 1888 onwards contined this work, as did *The Studio* magazine, established in 1893. This (and other magazines such as *The Artist* and *The Magazine of Art*) was a major showplace for modern decorative art with its illustrations, reviews and design competitions.

Arts and Crafts principles of manufacture tended to produce furniture of a certain simplicity of form, but this was often accompanied by elaborate detailing, especially of inlay and metalwork. Art Nouveau interior decoration took up these contrasts of simplicity and ornament, of flat surface and pattern. The emptiness of its rooms, compared with the aesthetic clutter, allowed individual decorative elements more prominence. CFA Voysey, architect and designer, took a more austere view than many but was not entirely untypical when he said, "Instead of painting boughs of apple trees on our door panels and covering every shelf with petticoats of silk, let us begin by discarding the mass of useless ornaments and banishing the millinery that degrades our furniture and fittings. Reduce the variety of patterns and colours in a room[6]."

6 Quoted in *The Studio* I, 1893, p234.

One way of reducing patterns and colours was to remove the dado and lower the frieze. The high style of *The Studio* preferred to panel the lower part of the wall to the height of the door. However, in spite of machine production, panelling was still expensive. Moreover, most people, renting rather than owning their houses and moving more frequently than they do today, were unwilling to spend a lot of money on items which they could not easily take with them. Wallpaper, therefore, remained popular. The patterns were often large, rhythmically swirling, highly stylised floral forms, although by the late 90s more formally organised, widely spaced designs with emphatic outlines were also common. It was important that the overall impression was flat — effects of shading or perspective were anathema.

In the 1880s and early 90s the colours used tended to be deep green-blues, ochres and dull greens but, increasingly, lighter, brighter colours became popular. In 1896 Mrs Panton was writing, "... we cannot possibly have too much real colour, and ..... far from demanding the timid compromises so dear to English folk, our climate and atmosphere clamour for real sealing-wax reds, deep oranges, clear yellows and beautiful blues."[7] And by the early twentieth century an even lighter impression was given by the tender greens, pale mauves, pinks and blues of the sparer patterns.

7 JE Panton, *Suburban Residences and How to Circumvent Them.* 1896, pp125—126.

The vertical emphasis of the wallpaper was contrasted with the horizontals of the wide frieze. Printed or stencilled, the frieze might continue the theme of the wallpaper or could employ a different motif. In the 1900s, rose trees or poppies, or landscape scenes in subtly shaded colours would decorate the top section of the room. For the floor, Oriental carpets, either genuine or modern adaptations, on varnished floors remained fashionable, but Art Nouveau designs were also used or very plain carpets with patterned borders. Upholstery and curtains were less voluptuous than before. Although the fabrics were richly patterned brocades, cut and printed velvets and bold cretonnes, frills and flounces were much less in evidence.

The convention of different treatments for different rooms remained in force: the drawing-room in a light key, the dining-room panelled, but the differences were not as marked. This was particularly true of the houses shown in *The Studio*. These were often country retreats and although it was still very important to keep the servants and service areas as separate from the living rooms as possible, a certain amount of informality in the latter areas was considered appropriate. MH Baillie Scott, for example, whose work was much featured in *The Studio* sometimes used the hall not just as an entrance to the house but as a multipurpose room[8]. This was a reference to the great baronial hall and the medieval note was very strong in Baillie Scott's work. He used oak panelling, low beamed ceilings, whitewashed rough plaster, massive stone or brick fireplaces, inglenooks and a minimum of heavy simple furniture. The fireplace was always a dominant feature, with an open grate, tiled facings and a great decorated copper hood or panels. Elaborate ornament was confined to areas of inlay, cutouts, or metalwork on the fireplace, furniture and doors. Although he did use coloured friezes, these were more often confined to the drawing-rooms and bedrooms which might also have patterned walls.

Voysey's interior work shared the simplicity and informality but employed a refined classical elegance with its slender uprights and pale colours. He too favoured low ceilings but reduced the decorative points still further. Although he continued to design his beautiful and spare wallpapers until the 1930s, he used them very little in his own work. It is interesting that *The Studio* championed Baillie Scott and Voysey but took a much more cautious attitude to the Art Nouveau of Glasgow. Although CR Mackintosh, Herbert McNair and the McDonald sisters also used contrasts of colour and decoration against plain surfaces, their delicate attenuations, elongations and extreme stylisations of natural forms were seen as suspiciously akin to the 'decadence' of Continental Art Nouveau. In spite of their success in Glasgow and their obvious influence on the Vienna Secession, their overall impact in England remained limited.

The unified schemes, custom designed even down to the door furniture and light fittings, that were featured in the art magazines

8   The Studio, XIX 1900, pp30–38.

9 op cit p228.

10 op cit.

were presented only as examples of the high style rather than as actual decorating advice. They had, of course, to be adapted to fit the merely prosperous pocket or the periodic redecoration. This could be achieved by painting the woodwork in plain pale colours and using the Art Nouveau wallpapers and friezes that were available for as little as 6d ($2\frac{1}{2}$ new pence) a piece. New Art furniture, stained green or fumed or limed oak with copper fittings, could be bought from shops such as Liberty in London or Wylie and Lochead in Glasgow. Beaten and repoussé metal light fittings, door furniture, fire irons and fenders would all add to the effect, as would a rather plain fireplace and overmantel of wood or cast iron decorated with copper panels or inlay. Fitted furniture, felt to be particularly appropriate for the 'quaint' treatment was, with machine production, becoming somewhat less expensive and more popular, especially for bedrooms where its hygienic (ie dust avoiding) and space saving qualities were valued. (To completely kit out a fitted bedroom would have cost about £70 or £80, according to HJ Jennings, in 1902).[9]

Of course, not everyone using Art Nouveau decoration took it on wholesale. Mrs Panton in 1896, although advising New Art furniture and wallpapers and throwing out the shelves and brackets and some of the furniture, still clung to her portières, dadoes, frilled curtains and potted palms.[10]

Fashionable styles did not have a great effect on kitchens, sculleries, servants' quarters and bathrooms, which were treated with more of a regard for cleanliness than with an eye to appearance.

Art Nouveau was predominantly an upper middle class style, but even in this market it was not the only choice. Rather than modern decoration, many people were still using historical styles, although it was noticeable that it was the simpler period forms that were popular. Elaborate 'English Renaissance' was giving way to 'Adam', 'Sheraton', 'Chippendale' and the more restrained French style of Louis XVI. Here too there were paler colours and less clutter. The all-too-revealing glare of electric light and concern for cleanliness no doubt played their part in simplifying decoration.

Art Nouveau reached its peak of popularity in the early 1900s but by then the Arts and Crafts ideals so influential in its development were beginning to support a style of greater and greater simplicity. The low ceilings and casement windows of Baillie Scott were transformed from their baronial splendour to cottage homeliness. This kind of rural plainness and some of the Arts and Crafts ideals have seen expression throughout the twentieth century, in the garden cities, public and private housing, and utility furniture, to name a few examples. But Art Nouveau was left behind as simply one fashionable style among many. It became too popular to bespeak 'good taste' and by 1910 had almost completely disappeared.

Lesley Hoskins

Bibliography

JH Walsh. *A Manual of Domestic Economy: suited to families spending from £100 to £1,000 a year.* G Routeledge & Co. 2nd edition, 1857.

Charles Eastlake. *Hints on Household Taste.* Longmans, 1872.

WJ Loftie. *A Plea for Art in the House,* one of the *Art at Home* series, ed. WJ Loftie. Macmillan & Co. 2nd edition, 1877.

RW Edie. *Decoration and Furniture of Town Houses.* C Kegan Paul & Co, 1881.

JE Panton. *Suburban Residences and How to Circumvent Them.* Ward & Downey, 1896.

HJ Jennings. *Our Homes and How to Beautify Them.* Harrison and Sons, 1902.

Ed PN Hasluck. *Cassell's House Decoration.* Cassell, 1908.

The Studio 1893 onwards.

The Studio Year-Book of Decorative Art. 1906—1925.

Modern British Domestic Architecture and Decoration. Studio supplement, 1901.

The Cabinet Maker and Art Furnisher. 1881—1902. (1902 onwards, *The Cabinet Maker and Complete House Furnisher*).

Modern Wall Decoration. The Decorative Art Journals Company Ltd, 1893.

Tim Benton and Sandra Millikin. *Art Nouveau 1890—1902.* The Open University Press, 1975.

Gillian Nayler. *The Arts and Crafts Movement.* Studio Vista, 1980.

N Cooper. *The Opulent Eye. Late Victorian and Edwardian Taste in Interior Design.* The Architectural Press Ltd, 1976.

Preparing for Art Nouveau: the evidence of an archive

Some time in the autumn of 1900, Rex Silver visited Paris. It was the year of the fifth great *Exposition Universelle,* in which Art Nouveau design triumphed. The special 'Paris Exhibition 1900' issue of the normally conservative journal *The Watchmaker, Jeweller and Silversmith* moves from pages of introductory advertisements for objects whose styles would often have been recognisable at the Great Exhibition of 1851 to a series of enthusiastic articles illustrated with photographs of objects designed by Tiffany and Lalique. Rex Silver's visit to Paris probably incorporated a desire to keep abreast of the latest Continental taste and to introduce his nineteen-year-old brother Harry to it, for he took Harry with him on this occasion and Harry was coming to the end of his period of training as a designer in the Silver Studio.

There may also have been an element of celebration in the visit, since Rex had reached the age of twenty-one in August 1900 and was now legally entitled to exercise the control of the studio which he had effectively possessed in practical matters and selling since his father's death five years earlier. As Arthur Silver's own team of designers left to take up freelance work (the most distinguished of them, Harry Napper, had gone in 1898, though he remained a friend and continued to sell designs through the studio) Rex and Harry were moving into the relationship which was to last until Harry's withdrawal from the concern in 1916, during the most difficult period of its affairs in the First World War. Rex would continue to act as business manager and Harry would be chief designer and coordinator of the design team's work: but with both brothers working in the closest harmony.

But the primary purpose of the 1900 visit to Paris, as it had been of Rex's visits in October 1898 and October 1899, was the selling of new designs. Harry might have a few days to look for inspiration and ideas in Paris, but Rex's notes show him touring Parisian firms assiduously before travelling on to Lille and Roubaix in northern France, where the Silver Studio was rapidly building up contacts with the expanding textile industry of the area. L'Art Nouveau had made few inroads at Roubaix as yet, but one of Rex's jottings suggests the beginnings of a shift of taste: 'Try some large Verdure designs for next year. Quaint and new but not too extreme'. Contacts were kept up, meetings in London arranged for the following winter, and a gratifying number of sales seem to have resulted from Rex's enterprise.

Enterprise had marked the Silver Studio's connections with foreign manufacturers from the very beginning, and though Arthur Silver died too early to reap the same benefits from his foreign contacts that he had from his energetic salesmanship in Scotland and the English provinces, he laid foundation which were of the greatest use to his sons. The sale of designs to northern France and Germany in the years before 1914, and to America in the 1920s were to form an important part of the Silver Studio's activities.

It might seem at first sight that a young designer setting up his own firm in 1880, with a wife and small children to support and a need for immediate income, was unlikely to be concerned with overseas taste and manufacture, and no doubt Arthur Silver's attention was chiefly focused on firms near his own doorstep at the beginning. But his thoughts were never purely insular: indeed he had grown up with, and had been in a sense produced by, a movement in design awareness which was as likely to work against Victorian British insularity as to support it. Arthur was born in 1853, the year of the 'World's Fair of the Works of Industry of All Nations' at New York; the first of the great international exhibitions of design and manufacture which were inspired by the success of the Great Exhibition. It was also the year in which Henry Cole's desire to have an archive of good designs available to stimulate British designers led to the gathering together of the Department of Science and Art's materials at South Kensington. The importance of this development for British design in the second half of the nineteenth century and far beyond cannot be overestimated. It vastly increased the body of material available for copying and adaptation by designers, and widened the range of styles to which a young designer was exposed. Arthur Silver spent long hours of study at the South Kensington Museum (later the Victoria and Albert Museum) and as late as April 1943 Rex Silver writes to his wife that despite War conditions, 'Studio work is still pouring in from all directions and I am detailing it out to myself and others as fast as I can. Yesterday I spent more than half a day with Bareham partly at the SKM and partly at the Studio, and started him well with a number of new ideas. This morning I did the same with Miss Lawrence, and tomorrow I link up again with Miss Koehler'.

Arthur Silver trained at Reading School of Art under the government-sponsored scheme for education or design in industry which Henry Cole had originated. When he went on to be articled to the London designer HW Batley he found himself working for a man who could develop the eclectic stylistic training which Reading had afforded. Arthur Silver's sketch books from the late 1870s show him designing furniture in the fashionable Queen Anne Revival manner of the time, and moving on to Neo-Adam, but he varied this with Japanese-inspired room schemes and furnishing details of the kind which Batley himself designed. Batley probably awoke Arthur Silver's interest in the then recently discovered art of Japan, and Japanese art (which Arthur collected: he was also an early member of The Japan Society) along with designs inspired by it from the hands of Walter Crane, EW Godwin, Christopher Dresser and lesser figures of the 1870s and early 1880s was the strongest single influence on Arthur Silver's development of an individual and distinctive form of design draughtsmanship, closely akin to and then indistinguishable from the forms and rhythms of emergent Art Nouveau.

Arthur Silver left HW Batley in 1880 to found his own freelance design studio at a time when increasing middle class affluence, new housing, growing public interest in furnishing taste and good design and the appearance of a whole range of new professional journals for architects, designers and manufacturers of home furnishings must have encouraged him to take the step. But an early paragraph in the interview which he gave to Gleeson White for *The Studio* in 1894 highlights a perhaps unexpected element in Arthur's decision: he explains why, in 1880, he felt the need for a design team to work under the control of a single artist-designer:

> 'Had such a system been worked before?'
> 'No doubt many Continental artists had found it answered their purpose. Indeed, at that time the large amount of commissions sent abroad aroused in me an intense desire to discern whether such an establishment could not be worked in England to counteract this habit and lead to the employment of British designs. In proof of its success, I may say that now commissions are coming to England from the Continent'.

The patriotic British designer wished to recapture opportunities for artists in his own country from foreign concerns. But from this to the acquisition of overseas commissions seemed a logical step. Insular pride might be bound up with commercial common sense, but at the same time Arthur was presupposing a shared taste at home and abroad, with the same kinds of design being acceptable to British and overseas purchasers.

Such an assumption also underlies the first communication that Arthur Silver is known to have had with an overseas agent, offering him a chance to sell designs and gain a reputation abroad. In October 1884 there came a letter fom Harry Wearne, written during a sales visit to New York. Wearne describes himself as 'connected with one of the first Continental houses of paper-hangings — Messrs J Zuber et Cie of Rixheim, Alsace' and his hope is that Arthur Silver may be interested in supplying wallpaper designs which Zuber can sell simultaneously on the English and American markets. He explains that his firm specialises in the more expensive, block-printed papers, and goes on to outline contemporary American tastes:

> 'I find that out here there is a great tendency for large flowing foliated patterns, but this is the market par excellence for the 'haute nouveauté', so, if you have in your mind anything of a very exclusive nature I would like to have the chance of seeing it first...'

A subsequent letter enlarges on American taste in expensive wallpapers:

> 'A bold Italian foliated motif, or Louis XIV, would be good, as, out here, they do not much care for set patterns: neither will they have designs with birds,

griffins, lions or leopards — no living thing, nor
anything of a heraldic character...'

Harry Wearne's letter probably marks the start of the Silver
Studio's connection with America. Documentation is,
unfortunately, very scanty indeed during the first years of the
firm's existence, but the number of nineteenth century trade and
visiting cards still in the archive suggests that before Arthur Silver
died in 1896, links with America were being established. No doubt
this was helped by (and perhaps sometimes achieved through) the
British manufacturers for whom Arthur worked, since their
products were achieving success in the States. At the 'World's
Columbian Exposition', Chicago, 1893, William Woollam's and Co
received an award for their wallpaper. In due course Arthur
Silver's 'skill as a designer' which had 'assisted in the production
and perfection of the exhibit' was recognised with the despatch of
an official display certificate which he framed and hung in the Studio.

Individual successes abroad were, inevitably, less important to a
designer than the growth of his reputation back at home; yet there
is no reason to think that the two were altogether unconnected.
But perhaps the most important factor of all was the coming into
being, as the market for good design in domestic furnishings grew,
of a tightly-knit community of late Victorian London-based
designers and manufacturers. The tightness of some of these
interconnections can be illustrated form the Silver-Aumonier
friendship. Arthur's friend Frederic Aumonier directed the firm of
William Woollam's, whose prize-winning wallpaper exhibit at
Chicago, 1893, Arthur Silver designed. Louisa Aumonier acted as
a part-time worker with the Silver Studio for some years in the
1890s, and shortly before Arthur's death the young Stacy
Aumonier (later to be well-known as a light novelist and
entertainer) joined the Studio team for a while. Older or better
established members of the London designers, and manufacturers'
group were willing to help the careers of those less well known
when their work seemed to deserve approval.

When Arthur Silver died, Walter Crane wrote, 'He was an able and
graceful designer and an amiable character'. In Arthur's lifetime he
had helped him towards membership of the more prestigious new
designers' associations and encouraged him to exhibit at the
annual exhibitions of the Arts and Crafts Exhibition Society from
1889 onwards. These exhibitions were well publicised in the
press, and Arthur was also much helped by his close friend
Gleeson White (first editor of *The Studio*) who wrote,
characteristically during Arthur's illness in 1896, 'If you are
sending anything to the Arts and Crafts you would like illustrated
in *The Studio* and I can save you any bother in the matter please
let me'. The same letter passes on the news that 'the Saunders
people' for whom Arthur had supplied some designs 'had a lot of
orders from France for silk when I was at the works in the early
spring and are, therefore, likely to be financially sound, though
slow payers.'

Help from Gleeson White at a time when *The Studio* was steadily attracting fresh attention in Europe was clearly of great potential value, and the friendly connections with some of the chief textile and wallpaper manufacturers of the 1890s were to last till Rex Silver's final years in the early 1960s: but opportunities to expand the studio's activities at home and abroad and to increase its reputation depended upon a constant supply of good designs in a variety of styles as well as on energetic publicity and marketing. Arthur Silver built up a remarkably efficient relationship with the press in the seven years which remained to him after the publication of his Silvern Series of photographs of historic textiles in the South Kensington Museum collection. These were to influence the development of British Art Nouveau styles in the early 1890s, but in 1889 they were hailed by the press as likely to be of use not only to British designers and manufacturers but also abroad. *The Glasgow Herald* of August 17, 1889 commented,

> 'The scheme just ready for presentation to the public is likely to arouse curiosity both at home and abroad, as the various state departments on the Continent analogous to our own South Kensington are likely to make use of it to augment their store of patterns from our own well-stocked museum, wherein lie hidden countless treasures practically inaccessible to those more immediately concerned manufacturers whose works are at a distance from them.'

Arthur's family at Reading saw to it that the paragraph was reprinted in the *Berkshire Chronicle* for August 24, 1889. A friend, if not Arthur himself, contrived to have it paraphrased in *The Artist* for September 1, 1889: this efficient circulation of publicity material accompanies several of the enterprises of Arthur Silver's last years, in addition to Gleeson White's coverage in *The Studio.*

But underpinning the publicity lay the constant provision of new designs in both traditional and contemporary styles. Arthur Silver genuinely believed that the designer must supply all the styles that the public asked for, while trying to raise public taste by executing every style to the best of his ability. An eclectic artist by training, he gradually assembled a team of specialists to work under his overall direction as work opportunities for the Silver Studio multiplied. A paragraph from *The Morning Leader* of August 20, 1892, advertising the forthcoming book *Practical Designing,* edited by Gleeson White (who probably supplied the publicity material on which the paragraph is based) remarks,

> 'Mr Silver's long and unique experience of designing should make what he has to say on the matter particularly valuable to students and decorative artists. The work produced from his studio is perhaps greater in amount and variety than that produced under the direction of any other one artist.'

It is perhaps significant of Arthur's awareness of stylistic change that it was at precisely this time that he took advantage of his increasing order book to employ two young men who showed a marked flair for emergent Art Nouveau styles. Arthur helped John Illingworth Kay and Harry Napper to become known by attributing their designs when they were shown at the Arts and Crafts Society exhibitions, and their work was publicised in *The Studio*. Their gifts for stylised pattern produced both a large number of distinctive designs of their own and a cross-fertilisation with Arthur Silver's own Japanese-inspired style of sinuous linear movement (generally shown as being caused by wind or water currents) playing upon plant and flower masses. They enriched Arthur Silver's own style and he, in turn, increased the range and vocabulary of theirs. Arthur Silver's encouragement was repaid after his death not only by the fine designs which they continued to produce, by Napper's direction of the design team and the training given to Harry Silver in due course, but also by the introduction as a supplier of designs for Liberty's metalwork of the distinguished Manx artist Archibald Knox. This was almost certainly Harry Napper's doing, and experience of Napper and Knox's work was crucial to the development of Harry Silver's style. He, from the opening years of the new century until 1916 was to be not only the studio's artistic director but also its most distinguished designer, producing in particular, Art Nouveau and Celtic designs which are, at best, in no way inferior to Knox's and Napper's own.

A design studio attracted talents (Arthur Silver received hundreds of applications for work each year), it accumulated photographs, books and journals (many Japanese-inspired designs taken from the magazines of the 1870s and 1880s survive in the Silver Studio Collection to this day) and both participation at exhibitions and actual sales tours helped in the acquisition and the spreading of knowledge concerning the latest trends in design. No evidence survives to show whether Arthur Silver travelled abroad, but from about 1892 he was selling designs to firms in Paris and northern France quite frequently: indeed in the last years of his life these sales represented a considerable part of his income. He collected foriegn illustrated material, especially coloured plates (he maintained that far fewer young designers had a sense of colour than a sense of form). His sons were to continue collecting French and German publications concerning design and decoration until the studio contracted the scale of its operations with the outbreak of the Second World War.

It must, however, be said that no Continental influences operated upon avant-garde English design trends in the 1890s comparable with the rage for Russian Ballet colours and forms immediately after the Great War, or the Art Deco style of the years around 1930, to which Rex Silver's team of designers had to adapt at the expense of a great deal of time and energy while sometimes sacrificing their inclination to do other kinds of work. The designer of the 1890s was scarcely troubled by international trends:

England led the way. French influence in the 1890s was merely historical, exercised through the adaptation of period styles. In progressive design the influence of Japan and the Japanese-inspired designers of the 1870s (Walter Crane and Christopher Dresser in particular) had blended with Morris's stylisation of natural patterns to provide a body of remarkable creative work which the Silver Studio was constantly learning from, adapting and developing. Macmurdo (especially influential on Illingworth Kay), Voysey (whom Napper strongly admired) and, via Gleeson White's enthusiasm and *The Studio,* the innovative linear inventiveness of Aubrey Beardsley (for whom John Illingworth Kay and Arthur Silver himself — a sign of continuing openness to new influences — had a real relish) all exercised strong and healthy diverse influences against which no Continental example could begin to make itself felt.

In his 1894 interview for *The Studio* Arthur Silver had shown pleasure that English designers had recaptured work from Continental studios and were now even selling designs abroad. Inevitably there was an element of insularity (as well as commercial awareness) in such an attitude, and it accords with a certain inward-looking tendency in the English design community as a whole in the 1890s. Perhaps this was inevitable, since certainly up until about the time of Arthur Silver's death in 1896 English design was in advance of that to be found overseas (though this superiority was on the brink of being challenged by the new developments taking place in France, Italy, Austria and elsewhere). Arthur Silver followed Gleeson White in appreciating the design brilliance of Aubrey Beardsley, but in general Gleeson White and the whole world of English design rejected the forms and the sense of moral unorthodoxy inspired by French art and literature of the Decadence.

Moral unease shows through Gleeson's dismissal of the attenuated forms of the Misses Macdonald's work at the Arts and Crafts Exhibition of 1896. On the strength of their elongated figure drawing he judges that the term 'the spooky school' is a 'nickname not wholly unmerited'. A year later he is able to praise Mackintosh's originality as an architect and decorator, but when he looks at Mackintosh's stylised and attenuated figures he is again wholly unable to come to terms with the style. In later years CFA Voysey was to show a comparable reluctance to equate his own designs with Continental Art Nouveau. Once again the objection seems to have been based on moral uneasiness concerning certain aspects of its treatment of the human form rather than purely decorative considerations.

In his book on Art Nouveau, Mario Amaya lists certain of its most significant sources: *anti*-historicism, Rococo and Oriental art, Celtic art, Japanese prints, architecture and furniture and a strong drive towards mysticism akin to that found in French Symbolist poetry. The Studio, as Arthur Silver left it at his death in October 1896, was experienced in all but one of these areas. Arthur's training had come late enough to escape the Gothicism of mid-century and the taste of the 1870s and early 1880s had exercised him in the elegant curves and swirls of eighteenth century decoration. Indeed his own designers were actively participating in a revival of the fashion for such designs at the time of his death: ultimately it would culminate in the neo-Adam vogue of the opening years of the twentieth century. The South Kensington Museum had played a decisive part in Arthur's training, and he had impressed the importance of constant reference to its richly diverse collections on his apprentices: he was now doing the same for his own children. The art of Japan had been a vital force in his own development and he had grafted its asymmetrical rhythms and movements onto the gifts for linear ornamentation of his most talented young assistants. His religion was Christian Science, and the gesso panel 'The Seven Days of Creation' which he had designed and Napper had helped to mould had shown, in the words of *The Builder* for January 27, 1894, 'discs symbolic of the Seven Days, upon winged spiral lines suggestive of infinite progression'. As the accompanying illustration and the actual panel show, the design, with its whirling disc patterns studding a larger spiralling motif, is closely akin to Art Nouveau in its fusion of strong linear form and structure with a constant impression of unending movement.

Of Marion Amaya's list of constituents to Art Nouveau's sources only the influence of Celtic art was lacking from the studio's repertoire of design influences when Arthur Silver died. It was added a couple of years later when Archibald Knox brought designs to be sold through the studio: and though both Harry Napper and Archibald Knox were soon to withdraw from the studio's affairs, Harry Silver's Napper and Knox-influenced designs were to keep the Silver Studio's output of Art Nouveau and Celtic designs at a very high level for as long as the vogue for these styles continued.

The two young men who visited Paris late in 1900 might not be as sympathetic with Art Nouveau in all its manifestations, or as well-informed about current work in some parts of Europe as the historian of today, but they are likely to have been as knowledgeable and as sympathetic towards Art Nouveau as any other young English designers of their generation. Their father's influence and the development of his ideas through the work of the design team which had built up would have seen to that. And the Silver Studio's busiest period of involvement with Continental manufacturers was just beginning. The vogue for Art Nouveau, which triumphed in 1900, might fade by the end of the first decade of the new century, but for the remainder of Harry Silver's time as a designer, and for the rest of Rex Silver's long life, they would be very much aware of design movements and sales opportunities abroad. Rex was to visit the great international exhibitions, to travel to America in the 1920s, to attend and sometimes to show at exhibitions at home. But the sense of excitement generated by European design at the beginning of the twentieth century and the stimulation offered by the great displays of the Art Nouveau period is perhaps best recaptured in a letter to Rex Silver from a man of Arthur Silver's generation, the minor artist and poet Edwin G Ellis. On June 24, 1906 Ellis wrote from Paris, urging Rex to visit the city between May 1 and July 1,

> 'because the decorative exhibits at the Salon would be very stimulating to you...If one went to the 'Grand Palais' for these only without looking at either the painting or the sculpture one could profitably spend a long morning among the curious glass cases...where glass, shells, jewels, metal, and lace are twisted about in wonderful shapes and colours to form either things to wear, to hang up, or to drink out of and put flowers in, upon which is spent a whole world of enthusiastic and enterprising imagination which is quite transforming the decorative mind of today'.

William Ruddick

NOTE: The material for this essay has been drawn from day books, letters, press cuttings and books in the Silver Studio Collection: the fact that this material was collected and preserved suggesting that it seemed, and remained, significant to the Silvers themselves.

105

110

129

167

135

157

34

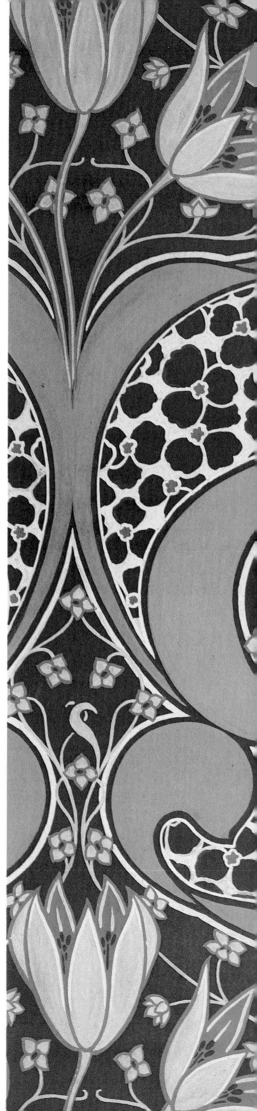

136

173

164

166

Silver Studio
Art Nouveau Designs
for Glasgow
Manufacturers

Because this exhibition is first being shown at the Hunterian Art Gallery, it is appropriate that we are able to include 'Mill Records' of some of the Glasgow firms that troubled to travel south and buy designs from the Silver Studio. Sadly, in most instances we are only able to show sketches for designs bought by these firms for, of course, the finished originals went to the purchasers. It is even sadder not to be able to include examples of some of the magnificent floral chintz designs bought by United Turkey Red in the 1920s or the elegant geometric designs that went to Morton's in the 1930s. However, we hope that these can be shown at a later date. It is obvious that the Silver Studio had a particularly good relationship with Glasgow firms, such as Wylie and Lochead and Templetons, and they bought some of the most avant-garde and splendid of the Studio's work. Alexander Millar, who was managing director of Templetons, lost no opportunity to praise Arthur Silver's carpet designs and sensitive use of colour. It was a particularly good instance of a very happy relationship between manufacturer and designer, which was a frequent occurrence in the late nineteenth century.

We are indebted to Juliet Kinchen and Elizabeth Arthur of Glasgow Museums and Art Galleries for providing this information. If anyone has additional information on these manufacturers, they would be delighted to receive it. Miss Kinchen is at Pollok House, 2060 Pollokshaws Road, Glasgow G43 1AT.

WYLIE & LOCHEAD

In the 1890s the Silver Studio supplied wallpaper designs to Wylie & Lochead of Glasgow, one of Britain's largest furnishing firms. Robert Wylie and William Lochead had joined forces in 1829 as cabinet makers and upholsterers. Their early rise to fame was as undertakers during the cholera epidemic of 1832, and this lucrative side of the business provided the financial basis for their rapid expansion and diversification in the field of house furnishing. As the French and English wallpapers which the firm began to retail sold well, it was a natural development to embark on the manufacture of such goods in the 1850s. The techniques involved were similar to those used for textiles and there was a local supply of ready trained block printers who were used to working with Paisley shawls and calico. From 1857 Wylie and Lochead supplemented their handmade goods with machine prints which were sub-contracted to a firm as far away as Lancashire.

Such an arrangement had obvious drawbacks and in 1862 they opened their own paper-staining factory in Glasgow equipped for both hand and machine printing. The firm was particularly well known for its stamped gold papers which it produced from the 1850s to the 1890s. In 1864 John Wylie had patented a method for their machine production, and other technical innovations followed such as the introduction of 'satinettes' in the 1880s. By 1882 Wylie & Lochead had the capacity to print in 15 to 20 colours simultaneously and were churning out 1,000 miles of paper a fortnight. Their export trade thrived (there was a landing stage on one side of the factory and a railway on the other), and their goods were distributed throughout Europe, America and the Empire by a network of agents.

Apart from employing in-house designers such as Arthur Gwatkin, Wylie & Lochead bought patterns from independent studios in Glasgow, London and Paris. While maintaining a range of traditional florid and historical styles they also purchased more adventurous designs from names like Christopher Dresser, George Haite, CFA Voysey, Owen Davis, Jessie King. In the 1890s their name became closely associated with the 'Glasgow Style' and one might have expected them to have purchased some of the Silver Studio's more Art Nouveau designs in preference to the very Morrisian patterns that were in fact selected.

Although they were the largest wallpaper manufacturers in Scotland this was never Wylie & Lochead's main or most profitable concern, and in 1899 they sold out to the Wall Paper Manufacturers Combine. The name of Wylie & Lochead continued to be used until the Glasgow factory was finally shut down in 1906.

UNITED TURKEY RED COMPANY
Alexandria Works, Dunbartonshire

This textile company was the largest bleaching, finishing, dyeing and printing concern in Scotland. It was formed in 1898 as an amalgamation of three existing firms — William Stirling & Sons (established 1723), John Orr Ewing and Archibald Orr Ewing (both established 1830). In 1960 the business was finally absorbed by the Calico Printers' Association.

JAMES TEMPLETON & CO;
JS TEMPLETON & CO

In 1841 James Templeton established a business in Glasgow, manufacturing chenille carpets by a process he had patented two years earlier with a weaver named Quigley. The carpets were an immediate success, and by 1855 a second factory was set up for the production of Brussells and Wilton carpets. This branch of the business was controlled by James Stewart Templeton (eldest son of the founder), and retained a separate identity until merged with the parent company in 1906. It was JS Templeton & Co which also manufactured silk curtains and chair covers. A fire in 1886 curtailed this aspect of the firm's production.

James Templeton Senior, his brother Archibald, and Peter Reid, who had been in partnership since 1843, all retired about 1878. From that time until his death in 1918 James Steward Templeton was the dominating force in the company. 1888 was an important year: Templeton secured the patent rights for a spool Axminster loom developed from the American Skinner loom. Thirty such looms were ordered and a new factory was built on Glasgow Green. The building was to William Leiper's design and modelled on the Doge's Palace in Venice. Spool steadily overtook the chenille weaving side of the business which was moved out to Kerr Street in 1901.

JS Templeton was actively involved in art education within Glasgow, both at the School of Art and the Glasgow and West of Scotland Technical College. His firm employed many of the students trained in these institutions such as Jessie MacLaurin, James Kincaid and Archibald Waker. Templeton also bought in designs from London and Paris produced by designers such as Walter Crane, Lewis F Day and CFA Voysey. The firm is known to have adapted wallpaper designs by Liberty and Shand Kydd. Arthur Silver's connection with Templetons seems to have been through a director, Alexander Millar. Alexander Millar refers to Arthur Silver in his lecture *Design in Modern Carpets* given in 1894 and published in *The Journal of the Society of Arts,* 20 April 1894.

DAVID BARBOUR & COMPANY

David Barbour formed a partnership with Robert W Miller in 1878 to manufacture tapestry curtains. The business expanded sufficiently to open a London warehouse at 78 Newgate Street in 1881, moving to 2 Paternoster Square in 1885. In 1881 another partnership with WA Lawson was established to form 'Barbour, Miller & Lawson, patent Axminster carpet, rug and oriental curtain manufacture.' They shared the Barbour & Miller facilities at Parkview Works, McNeil Street, Govanhaugh. Robert Miller left the partnerships in 1882 to work independently and was replaced by James W Anderson. Throughout this period the companies produced high quality goods which won gold medals at Paris in 1878 and Melbourne in 1881.

As trade expanded, the textile and carpet manufacturing business diverged when in 1890 David Barbour & Co was formed to manufacture chenille, tapestry, silks and muslins. Anderson, Lawson & Company continued to manufacture carpets and oriental curtains producing high quality designs by people such as Voysey.

David Barbour's new factory, the Renfield Works, King Street, Pollokshaws, Glasgow was noted for its modern equipment and healthy surroundings. The new weaving sheds accommodated approximately 100 hand and steam powered looms and were continuing to expand twelve months after opening. There were also offices, a packing and despatch department and well lit and decorated showrooms and stockrooms which supplied all the major British buyers, and a considerable export trade. In 1893 their new London branch at 4 Norwich Lane, Newgate was opened.

1   *Glasgow and Its Environs,* 1891 p150

In 1891 David Barbour & Co was described as a, 'Manufacturer of the finest qualities of tapestries in the richest combinations which for artistic designs and beauty of colourway are unrivalled... they are now engaged in producing an entirely new range of designs in chenilles by first class artists for the new season's trade.'[1] This probably refers to the 16 Silver Studio chenille designs purchased in 1891.

Barbour's purchase of a complete volume of South Kensington Museum photographs in 1892 suggest that they employed their own designers, however they continued to buy designs from the Silver Studio for the next 20 years. They also bought from other leading designers such as Lindsay P Butterfield and Alfred Carpenter.

After 1901 silk and muslin manufacture seems to have declined, although the firm continued to produce chenille and tapestry curtains and covers until they stopped trading in 1939.

ALEXANDER MORTON & COMPANY

This firm was formed in 1870 through the partnership of Alexander Morton (1844—1923) his elder brother Robert and his cousin Alexander Morton. The company produced cotton madras, machine lace curtains and later chenille fabrics. By 1890 carpet production was introduced which by 1905 accounted for a third of the firm's turnover. The carpets included traditional Axminster quality, 'Caledon' flat tapestry squares woven with bold two dimensional designs and in 1898 tufted 'Donegal' carpets made at Killybeggs.

Initially the firm's products were fairly traditional in style, however throughout the 1880s and 1890s designs by William Morris, Arthur Silver, Christopher Dresser, Lewis F Day, Walter Crane, Harrison Townsend and Lindsay Butterfield were introduced. The company had a long association with CFA Voysey, particularly between 1895 and 1906 when some of his designs were exhibited at the Arts and Crafts Exhibitions.

James (1867—1943) and Gavin (1865—1916), Alexander's two eldest sons, were in close contact with Glasgow artists and designers and James gave a lecture entitled, 'An Appreciation of William Morris' in March 1901 to the XL Club of Glasgow. This continuing association is seen in the carpet designed by Jessie Newbery, woven by Morton and exhibited at the Turin Exhibition in 1902. It is also seen in Jessie King's designs mentioned in the firm's records for 1903 and in the four carpet designs by Ann Macbeth illustrated in the 1914 *Studio Yearbook.*

In 1895 Alexander's brother left the company and a new partnership was formed between Gavin, James and their cousin Gavin. They moved to Carlisle in 1898 and in 1904 or 1905 introduced a range of printed furnishing fabrics which were produced by outside firms until 1912 when they set up their own hand block printing facilities. This range was given the brand name Sundour in 1906 and much of the dyeing for these fabrics was done by the United Turkey Red Company at Vale of Leven.

In 1908 Robert's son Gavin, the designer, left to form his own carpet manufacturing firm Blackwood, Morton & Company at Kilmarnock and in 1914 the partnership between the two brothers was dissolved. James became governing director of Morton Sundour Fabrics Ltd. He continued his interest in design in his appointment as a member of the Council of the Design and Industries Association. The same year, Gavin set up the Morton Manufacturing Company, Stirling.

JAMES BLACK & COMPANY

The calico and muslin printing firm of James Black, Drew & Co became James Black & Co on the retirement of Mr Drew in 1872. Their warehouse and showroom was at 23 Royal Exchange Square, Glasgow and the printworks at Dalmonach, Dumbartonshire. The company was taken over by the Calico Printers Association Limited in 1901.

JOHN GLEN

Established as calico printers in 1876 with works at Glengowan Printfield, Caldercruix near Airdrie and a warehouse at 15 Cochran Street, Glasgow. By 1902 the business had expanded to include muslin and silk printing. The warehouse moved to 7 South Frederick in 1905, to 128 Ingram Street in 1911 and finally to 243 St Vincent Street, Glasgow during the 1920s. The company closed in 1950.

GUTHRIE & McARLY

Thomas McArly formed a partnership with David Ernest Guthrie in 1879 to manufacture printed calico. McArly had trained for several years with the Glasgow branch of Charles Higginbothom & Co and then with James Shaw & Co, from about 1874 until 1879. He was also a partner in the Ferryfield Printing Co. David Guthrie died in 1900 and Thomas McArly retired in 1909 when the firm was taken over by the Calico Printers Association. Thomas McArly had many charitable interests and was a notable public figure. He held many appointments including president of the Glasgow Chamber of Commerce and chairman of the British Dyewood Co Limited. Guthrie & McArly continued as a branch of the Calico Printers Association at 4 West Regent Street until 1931.

LANG & COMPANY

Lang & Company was established in the early 1850s, the original partnership being Lang & Cousin. In 1877 Mr Cousin retired and the company was then run by James Lang and his two sons. They manufactured plain and fancy muslins, summer and evening dress fabrics, art curtains in 'Crete', madras, lace, oriental maunday and oriental bed sets and table covers. They specialised in curtain materials and printed Indian muslins. In 1886 they had premises at 146 and 150 Ingram Street and 4 John Street with a London branch at 16 Watling Street, managed by Thomas K Lang. The same year the company won a gold medal diploma at the Edinburgh International Exhibition for 'high art in oriental and madras curtains.' They exported widely to Europe, America, Australia and the West Indies. To cater for the demand for fine art fabrics, Lang's employed a large number of hand loom weavers in Upper Lanarkshire, Ayrshire and Northern Ireland.

In 1892 the company began producing machine embroideries at 18A Cook Street, Glasgow. During the 1920s the London branch moved from 12 Wood Street to Carey House, Carey Lane, London. By 1945, the only remaining Glasgow premises were at 150 Ingram Street. The firm closed in 1961.

THE MORTON MANUFACTURING COMPANY, STIRLING

This firm was founded by Gavin Morton (1865–1916) the eldest son of Alexander Morton, who together with his brother James was closely associated with Mortons of Darvel. Both Gavin and James were particularly interested in improving design standards and were in close contact with artistic circles in Glasgow and London. Although he produced carpet and textile designs himself, Gavin is not to be confused with his cousin Gavin (Robert Morton's son) who was a professional designer with Morton & Co.

In 1914, after a disagreement, Alexander Morton & Co was dissolved and Gavin left the partnership to set up a carpet factory at Cambusbarron near Stirling. Through his contact with the Newbery's and Ann Macbeth, Gavin's elder daughter Elsie became a student at the Glasgow School of Art in 1910. The intention was that Elsie would later become a designer at the Cambusbarron Carpet factory, but the sudden death of Gavin in 1916 caused the closure of the factory. During the short existence of the company, 31 designs were purchased from the Silver Studio.

MOIR & COMPANY

Moir & Company, calico printers, were established at 54 Gordon Street, Glasgow in 1879, moving to 92 Union Street in 1883. In 1887 they opened their Manchester warehouse at 16 Princes Street. By 1897 they had moved their Glasgow business to 2 West Regent Street where they remained as a branch of the Calico Printers Association from 1902 to 1912 after being taken over in 1901. The Silver Studio supplied them with six designs between 1891 and 1894.

Juliet Kinchin and Elizabeth Arthur

Catalogue

The following sequence has been observed for each catalogue entry. *Title* followed by *Dimensions*, followed by *Inscription*, followed by *Medium*, followed by *Date*, followed by *Description*. All dimensions are in centimetres, height before width.

1
Photograph of Arthur and Isabella Silver
9 × 11
circa 1890

Probably taken by Fred Hollyer who was a great friend of Arthur Silver. Hollyer photographed everyone of note in artistic London of the late 19th century.

2
Portrait of Rex Silver
25 × 20
circa 1910

Probably taken by Fred Hollyer

3
Photograph of Harry Silver
16.5 × 11.5
circa 1900

Harry Silver worked in partnership with his brother Rex as design manager of the Silver Studio until he joined the army in 1916.

4
Photograph of the drawing room of 84 Brook Green
26 x 20
circa 1905

This photograph, probably by the Arts and Crafts photographer Fred Hollyer, shows some of Arthur Silver's collection of Japanese prints and a little of *The Days of Creation* panel over the chimney piece.

5
Page from Arthur Silver's Sketch Book
22 × 18
Inscribed on fly leaf: *Arthur Silver / June 21 1873*
1873

This sketch book almost certainly dates from Arthur Silver's period at Reading School of Art. It contains an interesting selection of drawings of a wide variety of historic ornament. These include studies from pages of Owen Jones' *Grammar of Ornament* and numerous examples of French 18th century gesso work such as are shown on these pages.
SE 485

6
Sketch for a Gothic Cabinet
18 × 25
circa 1875

This drawing by Arthur Silver was doubtless executed while serving an apprenticeship to HW Batley. Although the drawing is undated, others in the sketch book are dated 1875. This example has been included to show Arthur Silver's awareness of mediaeval decoration, and which led him to look at material similar to that of William Morris in the Victoria and Albert Museum.
SE 486

7
Design for either a textile or wallpaper
58 × 72.5
Inscribed in Arthur Silver's hand, *Chrysmum / 24*
Gouache on cartridge paper
circa 1885

This exquisitely drawn design of large sprays of chrysanthemums in terracotta, different shades of grey, sage green on cream ground is by Arthur Silver. Although the naturalistic quality of the design bears a superficial resemblance to traditional chintzes, the use of chrysanthemums as a subject and the delicacy of the draughtsmanship show Arthur's interest in Japanese art.
SD 1266

8
Christmas Card
17 × 21.5
Inscribed: *Happy Christmas /* and on an inserted visiting card *Mr & Mrs Stahl, 135 Blythe Road, West Kensington Park W*
Pencil, watercolour on cartridge paper
circa 1885

Louis Stahl was one of the great late 19th century textile and wallpaper designers and a close friend of Arthur Silver's. Although this Christmas card may not at first appear to be of great interest, it has been included as an example of the interest in Roccoco decoration at the time and which has always been cited as a major influence on the development of Art Nouveau.
SD 9018

9
Design for a chintz
44.5 × 29
Inscribed: *467*
Pencil, gouache on cartridge paper
circa 1885

Chintz design by Arthur Silver with naturalistic flowers and acanthus leaves, and revealing his sensitive use of colour which was to play such an important part in the development of Silver Studio Art Nouveau.
SD 9016

10
Design for a wallpaper
57 × 48.5
Inscribed: *942*
Pencil, gouache on cartridge paper
circa 1885

This is an example of another important influence on the development of Silver Studio Art Nouveau — the work of William Morris and a close study of historic textiles in the Victoria and Albert Museum. This shows Arthur Silver looking at Flemish tapestries, though the colours are very smart 1880s 'Aesthetic'.
SD 9240

11
Design for a wallpaper
67.5 × 50
Inscribed: *No 1003A*
Gouache on cartridge paper
circa 1885

The first stirrings of Art Nouveau can be seen in the composition of this design, where parrot tulip sprays form scrolls. The colours — blues and purples on a cream ground are different from the normal terracotta and sage green of the 1880s and 90s.
SD 9243

12
Design for a wallpaper
55 × 45.5
Inscribed: *1147C*
Pencil and gouache on cartridge paper
1887

This simple design of sprays of carnations in ochres and blues on a cream ground shows a strong Christopher Dresser influence. Arthur Silver was a good friend of Christopher Dresser and both Rex and Harry worked in his studio in the late 1890s. (In turn Christopher Dresser apprenticed at least two of his sons at the Silver Studio.) Dresser was very important for his use of stylised botanical forms in his pattern designs.
SD 9247

13
Design for a wallpaper
58 × 40.5
Inscribed: *No 1109/1103 ?*
Gouache on cartridge paper
1888

This design by Arthur Silver is almost a straight reproduction of a Japanese print, with the minimum amount of adaptation to form a repeating pattern. This design is indicative of the very great interest of the Aesthetic English middle classes in Japanese decorative art. Note the use of terracotta and cream, which along with blue/green, sage green and ochre were the most fashionable colours in the late 80s and early 90s.
SD 9013

14
Volume I of *Artistic Japan*
33 × 25
Inscribed on the cover: *Artistic Japan / A Monthly Illustrated Journal of Arts and Industries / conducted by S. Bing*
1888

Bing's *Artistic Japan* was extremely important in introducing British designers to Japanese decorative art. It contained numerous articles on Japanese decoration and of course the illustrations were a particularly important influence. Arthur Silver subscribed to this journal until 1892.

15
Silvern Series photograph
62 × 62.5
Inscribed: *Chair Seat. Venetian 17th Century / 5670.79*
1889

One of Arthur Silver's highly successful photographs of objects in the Victoria and Albert Museum. They are very useful as they show us exactly the type of textile that inspired late 19th century designers.
SE 1727

16
Design for a Christmas card
40 × 35
Inscribed: *A Happy Xmas / A Rich New Year / A Silver*
Pen, ink and grey wash on cartridge paper
1889—90

An elaborate pseudo-Japanese design of lake, mountains, pine trees and flying cranes.
SD 9231

17
Design for a wallpaper
39 × 38
Inscribed: *1078*
Gouache on cartridge paper
1889—90

Although Japanese and Renaissance art were the two most important influences on English Art Nouveau, designers such as Arthur Silver ransacked the Victoria and Albert Museum for inspiration for patterns. Naturally, Near East and Middle Eastern Art was much studied. This design shows Arthur closely observing Persian embroidery.
SD 8484

18
Catalogue of anaglypta wallpapers
27.5 × 35
Inscribed on cover: *Anaglypta*
circa 1890

13

A catalogue of anaglypta patterns, a relief paper still manufactured today and which was enormously popular both in England and America. Arthur Silver produced many designs for this material including the one entitled *Japanese* p87. Both Voysey and Dresser designed for this firm, which listed its designers at the beginning of the catalogue.
SE 1013

19
Design for a Madras muslin
58 × 43.5
Inscribed: *No 1248 / For Madras*
circa 1890

Although this was produced as a wallpaper design, it would seem to have been used for woven Madras muslin, a very popular curtain material in the late 19th century home, and one for which Arthur Silver made a speciality of designing.
SD 8503

20
Design for a curtain lace panel
33.5 × 25.5
Inscribed: *L 68*
Gouache on cartridge paper
circa 1890

A typical Arthur Silver design of the late 1880s based on Renaissance ornament, acanthus leaves and scrolls in white on a grey ground.
SD 9019

21
Design for a Curtain Lace Panel
33 × 27
Inscribed: *L 69*
White and grey gouache on cartridge paper
circa 1890

Design of pheasants and sprays of stylised flowers for a lace curtain, showing an interesting alternative decorative treatment to catalogue number 20.
SD 9020

22
Design probably for a Woven Textile
54.4 × 40.3
Inscribed: *B.237*
Gouache on tracing paper
circa 1890

Beautifully painted design of parrot tulips in subtle greens and terracottas typical of aesthetic decoration. This is probably by Arthur Silver and is an extremely important work. It shows how a study of historic textiles influenced the development of Art Nouveau. It would seem to derive from 17th century needlework but has been given a

powerful organic quality in the vigorous drawing of the tulip stems and leaves.
SD 2905

23, 24, 25
Three printed furnishing textiles
each approx 18 × 25
circa 1890

These three printed calicos were sold by Liberty under the *Liberty Art Fabrics* labels. They resemble so closely the drawings by the Silver Studio for D Barbour that it is likely these were the result of a collaboration between Arthur Silver and Barbour.

26
Design for a printed textile
46.5 × 47
Inscribed: *852*
Pencil, watercolour on cartridge paper
1890

Delicately coloured design of chrysanthemums providing further evidence of Arthur Silver's delight in Japanese art, and the British middle class taste for Oriental decoration.
SD 8791A

27
Design for a printed textile
56.5 × 47.5
Inscribed: *842*
Pencil, watercolour on cartridge paper
1890

This design has been included as yet another influence in the development of Silver Studio Art Nouveau — the growing middle class desire to have light, delicate patterns for their upholstery. This is a typical late 19th century chintz pattern of sprays of flowers and leaves tied with ribbon knots.
SD 9244

19

28
Design for a printed textile
49.5 × 64
Inscribed: *813*
Pencil, black gouache on cartridge paper.
1890

This is a particularly important work for
showing the Japanese influence on Arthur
Silver's work. It would seem to be
directly adapted from Japanese prints and
shows birds, cherry blossom, fans and
chrysanthemums in black on a yellow
ochre ground.
SD 9012

29
Design for a printed textile
55 × 49.5
Inscribed: *843*
Watercolour, gouache, pencil on
cartridge paper
1890

This design, despite the representational
quality of the drawing has a lush, organic
quality which characterises so much Art
Nouveau pattern. It is based on a
conventional chintz pattern of sprays of
large poppies with daisies in the
background. (Arthur Silver was very fond
of using daisies in his patterns.)
SD 9245

30
Design for a Christmas card
32 × 38
Inscribed: *AS / A Merry Xmas / Best
Wishes 1890—91*
Pen and wash with a gouache border on
cartridge paper
1890

Arthur Silver's admiration for quaint
Oriental art was extended to creating this
pseudo-Japanese design for a Christmas
card of frogs having a picnic on a lily
pond.
SD 9232

31
Design for a printed textile
128.5 × 89.5
Inscribed: *738*
Gouache and watercolour on cartridge
paper
1890

This design was almost certainly by
Arthur Silver and shows how he was
influenced by Walter Crane, a great
friend of his, in some of his designs.
SD 3466

32
Design for a printed textile
59 × 54
Inscribed: *967*
Pencil, gouache on cartridge paper
1891

21

23

49

William Morris inspired design by Arthur Silver of large, naturalistic hydrangea flowers. Pale green and cream flowers with terracotta, green and brown leaves on a grey ground.
SD 8435

33
Design for a carpet
21.6 × 31
Inscribed: *No 459*
Gouache on cartridge paper
1891

Pretty miniature design by Arthur Silver, probably for Templeton. Scrollwork and representational flowers influenced by contemporary French carpet patterns.
SD 1419

34
Sketch for a carpet design
19.5 × 30.5
Inscribed: *1059E*
Pencil, red and blue crayon on detail paper
1891

Arthur Silver design for Templeton of Glasgow. Acanthus framed panels and sprays of chrysanthemums. Probably used as a scheme for a carpet filling.
SD 9017

35
Sketch for a carpet filling design
24.5 × 33
Inscribed: *530*
Pencil and crayon on detail paper
1891

Sketch for a carpet filling of honeysuckle, campanulas, cowslips, acanthus leaves

etc in red crayon and lead pencil. For Templeton of Glasgow.
SD 3648

36
Design for a wallpaper
51.5 × 45.5
Inscribed: *1111*
Gouache on cartridge paper
1891

Typical Arthur Silver wallpaper pattern with Art Nouveau sprays of daisies and chrysanthemums in ochre, sage green, pale blue on pale cream ground.
SD 3556

37
Embossed wallpaper catalogue
21.5 × 14
Inscribed on cover: *Tynecastle Canvas / Tynecastle Vellum*
1891

This catalogue illustrates some of Arthur Silver's more extravagant Renaissance revival patterns for embossed canvas wall coverings and which can be seen to have had a great influence in the development of Art Nouveau.
SE 1020

38
Design for wallpaper
57.5 × 44.5
Inscribed: *1471*
1891

This design shows the use of the sinuous curve characteristic of Art Nouveau patterns. Note, too, the use of typical Aesthetic Movement colours — pinks, olive green etc.
SD 8505

33

30

39
Design for a printed textile
45 × 29
Inscribed: *847*
Gouache on cartridge paper
1891

Simple Aesthetic chintz pattern of briar
rose in pinks and greens on a pale green
ground.
SD 8507

40
Four sketches for wallpaper designs
each approximately 15 × 10
Pencil, watercolour on cartridge paper
1891

These were all for Wylie and Lochead
wallpapers and are typical of the colours
fashionable at the time.
SD 4813, 4829, 4845, 4854

41
Four sketches for wallpaper designs
each approximately 15 × 10
Pencil, watercolour on cartridge paper
1891

These sketches were all for designs sold
to Wylie & Lochead in 1891. Note
particularly the top right design which
was for Wylie & Lochead's famous
Rokesley Poppy paper. This type of
wallpaper pattern was very popular in
smart middle-class drawing rooms in the
early 90s. A similar design was produced

by Voysey — *The Tokyo* wallpaper. The
other sketches shown here are also in
the fashionable olive greens and blues of
the period.
SD 4790, 4824, 4831, 4863

42
Design for a wallpaper
50 × 65.5
Inscribed: *1310* / stamped verso *A Silver/
Designer* / *84, Brook Green* / *London*
Pencil, gouache on cartridge paper
1891

A quaint Japanese print design very
similar in style to Arthur Silver's 1890
Christmas card, with water lilies, carp
and frogs. In pale blue, terracotta, green
and white.
SD 879

43
Design for wallpaper
67.5 × 48.5
Inscribed: *1383*
Gouache on cartridge paper
1891

Delicate chintz design of
chrysanthemums and pointed leaves in
venetian red, pinks, fawn, light olive
green and dark olive green.
SD 8504

44
Design for a printed textile
46.5 × 52
Inscribed: *968B*
Gouache on cartridge paper
1891

This design shows the strong
Christopher Dresser influence on the
Silver Studio's work. Dresser was a good
friend of Arthur Silver, (they probably
met through Gleeson White, the editor of
The Studio) and Rex Silver worked for a
short time in his studio, where he may
have met Archibald Knox. This design
has panels of conventionalised flowers
(Dresser's speciality) and shows a
Persian/Moorish influence.
SD 3588

45
Design for a printed textile
47 × 45
Inscribed: *802*
Gouache on cartridge paper
1891

Another example of the very great
influence of William Morris on the work
of the Silver Studio. This design is
derived from a study of 17th century
English embroidery and features strap-
like leaf scrolls and simple
chrysanthemum flowers.
SD 3609

46
Sketch for a wallpaper design
17 × 17.5

38

47

45

Inscribed: *1307*
Pencil, gouache on cartridge paper
1891

For Wylie & Lochead, a design of a large
poppy in pink and purple-red.
SD 4785

47
Design for a wallpaper
53 × 45.5
Inscribed: *No 939*
Pencil, watercolour on cartridge paper
1891

Extremely pretty Japanese-influenced
design by Arthur Silver of apple blossom
in pink, red and white on pale blue
ground. This type of design was much
admired by writers on decoration in the
80s and 90s and was probably intended
for Libertys.
SD 9011

48
Design for a printed textile
60.5 × 50.5
Inscribed: *949*
Watercolour, gouache on cartridge paper
1891

Probably for a chintz for a firm such as
Stead McAlpine. Although this is a
traditional chintz pattern — bunches of
multi-coloured flowers on a light ground.
Note Arthur Silver's sensitive and
delicate use of colour.
SD 9014

49
Three sketches for a printed textile
design
Each 25 × 20
Inscribed: *1061*
Pencil and gouache on cartridge paper
1892

These were sketches done by Arthur
Silver for a design which was
subsequently sold to the Glasgow
manufacturer D Barbour. They consist of
flower heads on a background of
acanthus leaves, and indicate yet again
the use of tertiary colours.
SD 5483

50
Design for a printed furnishing textile
53 × 52
Inscribed: *No 1105*
Pencil, watercolour on cartridge paper
1892

Design of chrysanthemum sprays on a
background of motifs from Japanese
prints — a good example of the Japanese
influence on Silver Studio work. Pale red
and ochre flowers with grey/blue leaves
on a grey and white background.
SD 9238

52
53
60

52

51
Two sketches for designs for wallpaper
15.5 × 12.5
Inscribed: *1550 / 1551*
Pencil, gouache, watercolour and gold
paint on cartridge paper
1892

The wallpaper design sketches for Wylie
& Lochead. The upper design is of a
spray of roses in moss green and brown
on a gold background. The lower is of a
spray stylised flowers and leaves in
terracotta, pink and gold on an ochre
ground.
SD 8295, 8297

52
Design for a printed textile
67 × 49
Inscribed: *1137B*
Gouache and pencil on cartridge paper
1892

This is a typical John Illingworth Kay
textile design, with bunches of small
brown flowers on twisting stems on
cream ground.
SD 8552

53
Design for a printed textile
63 × 50
Inscribed: *1046*
Gouache and pencil on cartridge paper
1892

Design of flowers and leaves on curved
sprays. Two colours — cream on a dark
blue/grey ground. This is a good example
of the Silver Studio adapting for cheap
textiles the type of chintz design first
made popular by William Morris.
SD 8483

54
Two sketches for wallpaper designs
8.5 × 10
Inscribed: *1571 / 1106*
Pencil, gouache on cartridge paper
1892

Two sketches for wallpaper designs for
Wylie & Lochead. The upper is based on
a poppy and leaf motif in bright blues and
pale olive green. The lower is of a spray
of carnations and serrated leaves in
blues, light ochre on a duck-egg blue
ground.
SD 5529, SD 8279

55
Three sketches for printed textile designs
Each approximately 18 × 12
Pencil, watercolour on cartridge paper
1892

These delicate sketches for D Barbour all
show a strong influence of Near Eastern
textile patterns.
SD 5477, 5478, 5481

56
Four sketches for printed textile designs
Various sizes
Pencil, gouache, watercolour on
cartridge paper
1892

These sketches for D Barbour & Co are
typical of Silver Studio artistic furnishing
textile designs of the early 90s. Note the
delightful use of tertiary colours and
stylised plant forms.
SD 5499, 5500, 5506, 5507

57
Two sketches for printed textile designs
Both 20 × 20
Inscribed: *No 1163 / 1163 CR*
Gouache, pencil and crayon on cartridge
paper
1892

These two sketches for Barbour
furnishing textile designs were by Arthur
Silver and based on iris flowers and
leaves. Yet another instance of Oriental
art influencing Silver's designs. The
design on the left is in terracotta and
olive green, the right in ochre and blue/
green.
SD 5569, SD 5570

58
Two sketches for printed textile designs
20.5 × 11.5 and 29 × 22.5
Inscribed: *1041 / 1074*
Pencil, gouache and watercolour on
cartridge paper
1892

These are two charming sketches for
designs which were bought by
D Barbour. Both show the importance of
Renaissance decorative art in the use of
the acanthus leaf and the tertiary colours
which were thought to be so much more
artistic than the colours of aniline dyes
which were such a feature of mid-
Victorian textiles.
SD 5503, SD 5586

59
Designs for a wallpaper filling and frieze
57 × 68.5 and 44 × 59.5
Inscribed: *1563*
Gouache on cartridge paper
1892

These designs are very much in the
Aesthetic movement tradition and reflect
the work of designers such as Bruce
Talbert and Christopher Dresser.
SD 8, SD 8491

60
Design for a printed textile
54.5 × 50
Inscribed: *1087A*
Gouache and pencil on cartridge paper
1892

Heavy, early Art Nouveau design for a
furnishing textile with sprays of pink,
yellow and brown flowers on a dark
brown ground. Here we can see that
Arthur Silver has been observing 18th
century Indian chintzes in the Victoria
and Albert Museum and giving them the
rich dark colours fashionable at this
time.
SD 8493

61
Design for a chenille curtain
128 × 72
Inscribed: *1307*
Gouache on squared paper
1892

Heavy, early Art Nouveau pattern of
poppies and acanthus leaves sold to
D Barbour of Glasgow for a chenille
curtain.
SD 9229

62
Sketch for a rug design
35 × 23
Inscribed: *560*
Watercolour and pencil on cartridge
paper
1892

Chinoiserie design by Arthur Silver of
chrysanthemums, cherry blossom and
bamboo in pale blue, ochre, reds, pink
and green on a fawn ground.
SD 8852

62

63
Three sketches for printed textile designs
Each 15 × 13
Pencil, gouache on cartridge paper
1892

Three sketches for designs sold to
D Barbour. The sketch on the left is
inspired by Persian embroidery, the
other two are closer to traditional
English patterns, but note the exciting
use of colour — pinks, reds, sage green
on dark blue ground.
SD 5479, 5482, 5573

64
Sketch for a printed textile design
19 × 14.5
Inscribed: *1076*
Pencil, watercolour on cartridge paper
1892

Small sketch for D Barbour & Co which
is useful for showing the range of colours
which appealed to commercial
manufacturers at this time. Yellow,
ochre, olive and dark green on a cream
ground.
SD 5505

65
Two sketches for printed textile designs
Each 16 × 15
Inscribed: *1072 / 1054*
1892

Two sketches of large, stylised flowers
and leaves for designs for the Glasgow
firm D Barbour & Co. Note the dark,
sombre colours — chocolate brown,
beige, dull green and blue.
SD 5480, SD 5498

66
Printed linen
26 × 22
1892

William Morris influenced furnishing
fabric produced by O'Hanlon from a
design probably by Arthur Silver. In pale
blues, terracotta, grey on white ground.
ST 313

67
Reversible machine printed cotton
10 × 20
1892

A Silver Studio design for Liberty of
Japanese style flowering branches and
medallions on fretwork ground in deep
blue on white.
ST 322

68
Woven silk tissue
23 × 14
circa 1892—95

102

74

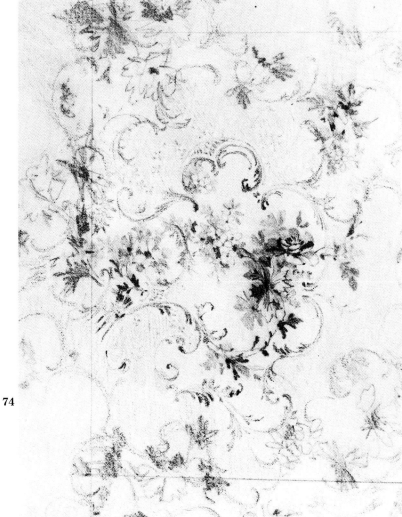

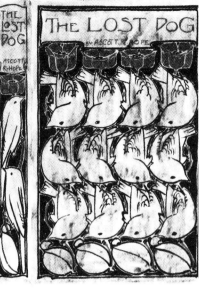

96

A typical Silver Studio Aesthetic design of stylised irises in greens, blues, terracotta on sage green gound. A very early work for the French firm of Leborgne.
ST 327

69
Woven wool and silk doublecloth
18 × 34
1892–3

An Aesthetic design probably by Arthur Silver of large stylised irises in sage green and gold on grey/green background.
ST 324

70
Design for a printed textile
69 × 58
Inscribed: *1067B*
Gouache on cartridge paper
1892

This design uses that most *fin-de-siècle* of flowers, the lily, with sinuous leaves and stems forming an ogee panel. The predominant colour is green with muted yellow for the lilies.
SD 8487

71
Design for a wallpaper
49 × 36
Inscribed: *1617*
Pencil, watercolour on cartridge paper
1892–3

Pattern of wild rose briars with single flowers, in pinks and browns on buff ground. A delicate, chintz design which would have been ideal for an Aesthetic bedroom.
SD 9015

72
Three sketches for wallpaper designs
13.5 × 12.5, 11.5 × 8.5, 14.5 × 20.5
Pencil, gouache and watercolour on cartridge paper
1892, 1893, 1898

These were all for designs for wallpapers sold to Wylie & Lochead during the 1890s. Note particularly the lower example, which was for a sanitary wallpaper (viz a paper printed with engraved copper rollers to produce a smooth, varnishable surface).
SD 5831, 8230, 8278

73
Design for a carpet
27 × 21
Inscribed: *used / 644*
Pencil and crayon on detail paper
1893

This early Art Nouveau design of leaf panels containing sprays of stylised buttercups might well have been by Harry Napper. For Templeton carpets.
SD 3946

74
Design for a carpet
29 × 21
Inscribed: *1093 / 687 / used*
Pencil and crayon
1893

A roccoco-inspired design for Templeton carpets of scrollwork and sprays of daisies.
SD 3953

75
Design for a carpet centre
32 × 19.5
Inscribed: *643 / used*

Pencil, charcoal and crayon on detail paper
1893

Sketch for a design sold to Templeton carpets of chrysanthemum flowers and large leaves in red crayon, pencil and charcoal.
SD 3951

76
Design for a printed textile
51 × 51
Inscribed: *1304*
Charcoal, gouache on detail paper
1893

This is possibly for a Liberty printed velvet and is an early example of Harry Napper's highly stylised Art Nouveau designs. The lower centre section is coloured yellow, terracotta, plum, ochre, green, blue on blue-green ground. This is particularly important work, because of the date at which it was executed. Note, too, the richness of the colours used.
SD 9239

77
Design for a printed textile
51 × 81
Inscribed: *1269*
Pencil, gouache on cartridge paper
1893

William Morris's wallpapers and textiles were very fashionable throughout the 1890s, and the Silver Studio did many designs that show the influence of his work. This is very typical. Two trial backgrounds are used in this design — dark blue/green and cream.
SD 9237

78
Three sketches for carpet designs
each 30 × 20
Pencil on cartridge paper
1893

Three sketches for carpets for Templeton
of Glasgow.
SD 3955, 3956, 3959

79
Design for a wallpaper
65.5 × 48
Inscribed: *1722*
Gouache and pencil on cartridge paper
1894

Design of a cluster of four yellow irises
on a light grey/green ground.
SD 8499

80
Sketch for a printed textile design
22 × 14.5
Inscribed: *1441*
Pencil and gouache on cartridge paper
1894

Design for a two-colour printed
furnishing fabric of kingcup flowers and
leaves in green on a cream ground.
Probably by John Illingworth Kay for
Barbour of Glasgow.
SD 6663

81
Design for a carpet
29.5 × 21
Inscribed: *728 / used / 496*
Pencil and red crayon on cartridge paper
1894

A landscape design for a carpet or rug.
Stylised trees and flowers form a
framework for a landscape.
SD 3952

82
Design for a carpet filling
46 × 71
Inscribed: *684 / used*
Gouache on squared cartridge paper
1894

Part of a design sold to Templeton of
Glasgow in 1896 for 6 guineas (see
catalogue number 83).
SD 9234

83
Design for a carpet border
63 × 44.5
Inscribed: *684*
Gouache on squared cartridge paper
1894

Part of a design sold to Templeton of
Glasgow in 1896. The design is of globe

flowers and leaves, and is a typical Art
Nouveau border design similar to that
used for wallpaper friezes. The colours
are sage greens, cream and terracotta.
SD 9235

84
Part of a design for wallpaper
18 × 18
Inscribed: *1865*
Pencil and watercolour on cartridge
paper
1894

Here the Silver Studio is adapting the
work of Kate Greenaway for a nursery
wallpaper. The Silver Studio Collection
also contains correspondence in which
Arthur Silver obtained permission to use
Tenniel's illustrations for *Alice in
Wonderland* for a similar purpose.
SD 8381

85
Design for a carpet
30 × 22
Inscribed: *1237 G. / 735 / used*
Pencil and crayon on detail paper
1894

Persian-influenced design of acanthus
scroll leaves in brown crayon. For
Templeton carpets.
SD 3950

86
Illustration of *The Days of Creation*
Gesso Panel
38 × 25.5
Inscribed: *Gesso Panel for Chimney
Piece* etc
1894

Designed by Arthur Silver and executed
by Harry Napper. The original is in the
possession of Arthur Silver's grand-
daughter, Mrs Erica Haxworth. It was
exhibited at the Arts and Crafts
Exhibition of 1893.

87
Four sketches for wallpaper designs
each approximately 15 × 13
Pencil, watercolour, gouache on
cartridge paper
1894–1897.

Four sketches for wallpaper designs sold
to Wylie & Lochead over the period
1894–1987. The lower centre design is
the earliest with large areas of flat,
tertiary colour. The two uppermost
designs show British Art Nouveau was
becoming increasingly hard-edged and
stylised.
SD 5842, 5833, 8367, 8372

88
Design for a printed textile
73 × 65.5
Inscribed: *No 1597*
Gouache on cartridge paper
1895

This design is almost certainly by John
Illingworth Kay and is based on cowslips
and lilies with sinewy stems and
spiralling leaves. In yellows and greens
with terracotta on a deep blue ground.
SD 3522

89
Design for either a textile or wallpaper
53.5 × 53.5
Inscribed: *486 & £3*
Gouache on cartridge paper
circa 1895

Typical Silver Studio Art Nouveau of the
mid-1890s, and probably by Arthur
Silver. The design is of lilies in parallel
vertical curving lines. Bright yellow,
olive green on a light and dark blue
ground.
SD 3581

90
Design for a printed textile
90 × 72
Inscribed: *476*
Pastel on tracing paper
Circa 1895

The flat, decorative treatment of this
design of peacocks would suggest the
work of Harry Napper. The Silver Studio
often incorporated peacocks in their
designs during the period 1880–1910.
SD 9228

91
Catalogue of stencil friezes
26.5 × 10
Inscribed on cover:
*Some notes on stencilling / with special
reference to / its novel application /
fabrics now being exhibited at 26 Garlick
Hill / EC by Rottmann & Co and / Arthur
Silver*
1895

This catalogue was for an exhibition to
publicise the joint venture between
Arthur Silver and Alexander Rottmann to
popularise the recently revived art of
stencilling. It was an ambitious project
which resulted in a great deal of publicity
for the Silver Studio. Arthur was given
considerable help and encouragement by
his old friend, the editor of *The Studio*
Magazine, Gleeson White. Gleeson
White had already interviewed Arthur in
1894 for an article entitled *A Studio of
Design*. For a second consecutive year,
Arthur was to be the subject of a lengthy
article in *The Studio* called 'Stencilled
Fabrics for Decorative Wall Hangings.'
There were numerous articles in the
press and the exercise did much to

establish the Silver Studio reputation. The stencilling venture was carried out in conjunction with Rottmann & Co. Alexander Rottmann was managing director of a firm that imported and manufactured Japanese leather and grass papers, and which had offices in Garlick Hill, in the City. Critics were delighted by this happy partnership between manufacturer and designer. The stencils themselves won the immediate approval of protagonists of the Arts and Crafts movement by the honesty with which Arthur Silver employed the stencil plates. Rather than camouflage the joints (ties) of the stencil plates, he incorporated them with the design.
SE 502

92
Page of illustrations of stencil friezes
38 × 50.5
Inscribed: *Designs for Execution in Stencil — By Arthur Silver*
1896

The Builder published Arthur Silver's lecture to the Architectural Association in 1896 on *The Modern Stencil and its Application to Interior Decoration* and included a page of examples.
SE 1726

93
Stencil frieze
48 × 57
Distemper on jute paper
1894/5

This was probably designed by John Illingworth Kay who was actively involved in the production of many Silver Studio friezes. He subsequently ran the stencilling department of Arthur Sanderson. The drawing of the tulips is very typical of his style and the use of colour is very sensitive — sage green, orange, blue-green and brown.
SW 2013

94
Stencil frieze — *The Richmond*
82 × 213
Inscribed: *The Richmond / No 1202 / Stencilled at the Silver Studios / Rottmann & Co Silver Stencil Series*
Distemper on Japanese grass paper
1895

The frieze was probably designed by Harry Napper and is of stylised poppies in red and green on cream grass paper.
SW 1557

The following designs (Catalogue numbers 95—98) were for Blackie & Sons and would appear to be very much the work of John Illingworth Kay and Harry Napper, executed over the period 1895—97. The connection was

undoubtedly established by Arthur Silver and Talwin Morris who was art director for Blackie during this period. Talwin Morris had lived in Reading and might well have met Arthur Silver there, but more likely Gleeson White introduced them in his capacity as editor of *The Studio*.

95
Two designs for Blackie's Book Covers
Each 30 × 26
Watercolour, gouache on detail paper
1895—97

Both are for Mrs Herbert Martin's *The Two Dorothys*. The design on the left was probably by John Illingworth Kay who had sold designs for book covers as early as 1893 to the London publishers Elkin, Mathews and John Lane, and had been highly commended for his cover designs for *The Studio* magazine in 1893 (see *The Studio* Vol 1 1893 p 204)
SD 1090, 1086

96
Two designs for Blackie's book covers
Each 30 × 26
Inscribed: *The Lost Dog / by Ascott R Hope*
Watercolour and gouache on detail paper
1897

Both designs were for Blackie but do not appear to have been sold or used. The design on the left would almost certainly be by Harry Napper. The stylised flowers of the upper border are typical of his work.
SD 1072 & 1085

97
Design for a Blackie's book cover
29 × 25
Inscribed: *The Youngest Princess / Jennie Chappell* and in pencil *The Hawthorn Series 01 1/-*
Water colour and gouache on detail paper
1897

This would appear to be by John Illingworth Kay and is of stylised trees forming a panel containing the title, with

bird and landscape. In pink, white and green.
SD 1091

98
Design for a Blackie's book cover
29.6 x 26.7
Inscribed: *Adventures in Field & Flood* and in pencil *05082*
Pencil and charcoal on detail paper
1897

Design of stylised tree with landscape including river and sailing barge. Probably by John Illingworth Kay
SD 1088

99
Design for a wallpaper
62.5 × 47.5
Inscribed: *2062*
Gouache on cartridge paper
1896

This design is typical of the Silver Studio's contribution to the British Art Nouveau. Sprays of flowers and curving stems in subdued colours — ochre, terracotta, sage green etc.
SD 9242

100
Design for a printed furnishing textile
70 × 58.5
Inscribed: *1726*
Gouache on cartridge paper
1896

Harry Napper design or poppies and buttercups in browns, pinks and terracotta. Note the flattened flower forms which are characteristic of Napper's work.
SD 9236

101
Design for a printed textile
60 × 59
Inscribed: *1609*
Gouache on cartridge paper
1896

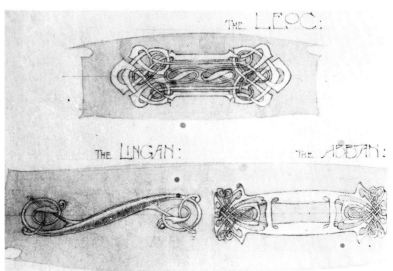

A typical John Illingworth Kay Art Nouveau design. Like so much of his work it is based on a Japanese landscape of stylised trees and irises. In greys, olive green and pale grey/cream.
SD 3523

102
Design for a wallpaper
59.5 × 53.5
Inscribed: *2066*
Gouache on cartridge paper
1896

Design of curving lines of strap-like leaves and large cow-parsley flower heads. In pale green, ochre and orange on cream ground. This is almost certainly the work of John Illingworth Kay — the flower heads in particular are typical of his style.
SD 3547

103
Design for a printed furnishing textile
61 × 60.5
Inscribed: *1647*
Gouache on cartridge paper
1896

Design of pink tulips on alternate bands of light and dark green leaves in vertical wavy lines. Two greens, venetian red and pink.
SD 8550

104
Design for a carpet
56.5 × 83.5
Inscribed: *No 997*
Gouache on cartridge paper
1896

This shows the influence of William Morris on Arthur Silver's carpet designs. Heavy, stylised flowers and leaves in dull colours — grey/blue, ochre, brown, black and terracotta. It is typical of the carpet designs sold to Templeton of Glasgow in the 1890s.
SD 1264

105
Design for a printed furnishing textile
73 × 63
Inscribed: *1849*
Gouache on cartridge paper
1897

Chintz design probably by John Illingworth Kay. Note the typical Silver Studio Art Nouveau upward spiralling sprays — daisies, carnations etc. In terracotta, electric blue and yellow on sage green ground.
SD 1258

106
Sketch for a wallpaper design
20.5 × 12.5

Inscribed: *2308*
Pencil, watercolour on cartridge paper
1897

Sketch of curving leaves executed to imitate stained glass, in blues, yellows, sage green
SD 5843

107
Design for velvet
58.5 × 43.5
Inscribed: *No 710 / For Genoise /11750*
Pencil, gouache on tracing paper
1897

Design of peacocks on flowering branches sold to Leborgne in March, 1897 for 6 guineas. Arthur Silver had started selling designs to France as early as 1893/4. By 1900 Rex Silver was selling far more designs to France than in Britain.
SD 9249

108
Design for a printed textile
70.5 × 62.5
Inscribed: *1837*
Gouache on cartridge paper
1897

This design shows the continuing influence of William Morris. Curving stripe and parallel panels of buttercups and leaves in yellows and blues on dark green ground.
SD 3538

109
Design for a printed textile
61 × 50.5
Inscribed: *No 1784*
Gouache on cartridge paper
1897

This shows how organic Art Nouveau gradually became more formalised. Thistle-like flower enclosed in an ogee-shaped panel of acanthus leaves. Terracotta, sage green on background of two shades of dark blue.
SD 3557

110
Design for a printed textile
66 × 59
Inscribed: *1854*
Gouache on cartridge paper
1897

Typical Harry Napper Art Nouveau design of poppies and acanthus leaves. Note the rich use of colour, with pink and pale green against a midnight blue ground.
SD 3546

111
Design for a wallpaper frieze
42 × 71
Inscribed: *2287*
Pastel and pencil on detail paper
1897

This design is very interesting as it shows how roccoco decorative art influenced British Art Nouveau. The components of this design — roses, chrysanthemums and roccoco scrolls, are all traditionally drawn but arranged so that the scrolls form waves.
SD 8571

112
Design for a printed textile
58 × 52
Inscribed: *1755*
Gouache and pencil on cartridge paper
1897

A delightful example of Silver Studio Art Nouveau by Harry Napper. Sprays of chrysanthemums and asters branching off a main S-shaped stem. Note the sharp outlines to the flowers and leaves which characterise Harry Napper's work. In pinks, browns, greens and ochre on a deep blue ground.
SD 8541

113
Design for a printed textile
80 × 63.5
Inscribed: *1841*
Gouache and pencil on cartridge paper
1897

Very stylised Art Nouveau design which is probably by Harry Napper. Large, thistle-like flowers and parallel lines of curving acanthus leaves. In greens, blue, grey, brown, apricot on mid-blue ground.
SD 8542

114
Two sketches for wallpaper designs
13 × 12.5 and 14 × 14
Inscribed: *2409* and *2357*
Pencil, watercolour on cartridge paper
1898

Two very stylish Art Nouveau wallpaper sketches, probably by Harry Napper for Wylie & Lochead. The lower one in particular is typical of Silver Studio Art Nouveau of the late 90s and early 1900s. Note the use of a light ground which became particularly popular after 1900.
SD 5830, 5634

115
Guild of Handicraft catalogue
26 × 20
Inscribed on cover: *The Guild of Handicraft Ltd / Silversmiths & Jewellers*

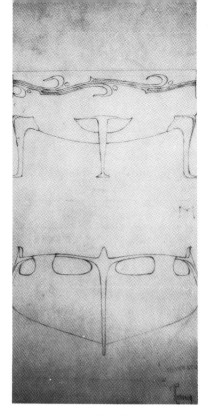
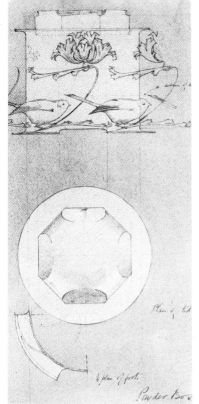
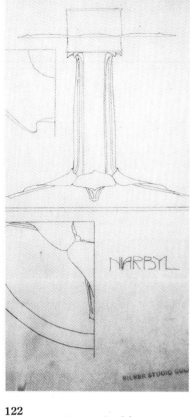

118
120
121

by appointment to Her Majesty the Queen
circa 1900

This is a fully illustrated catalogue (78pp) of CR Ashbee's Guild of Handicraft metalwork. This provided considerable inspiration for the Silver Studio's designs for Liberty metalwork.
SE 1060

116
Liberty & Co catalogue
18.5 × 24.5
Inscribed on cover: *Yule Tide Gifts*
1901

This catalogue includes numerous illustrations of metalwork from Silver Studio designs (see particularly pp 52–53).
SE 463

117
Three designs for silver brooches
14 × 23.5
Inscribed: *The Leoc / The Lingan / The Abban*
Pencil and watercolour on detail paper
circa 1898–1900

These brooches are illustrated in Liberty's *Cymric Silver* catalogue of circa 1900. The designs are very complex Celtic patterns and are almost certainly the work of Archibald Knox.
SD 8170

118
Two designs for silver bowls
24.5 × 21.5
Inscribed: *Maya /Romany*
Pencil on tracing paper
circa 1900

These are illustrated in the Liberty *Cymric Silver* catalogue of circa 1900 (see pp 58–59 and pp 62–63). The shapes are typical of Archibald Knox and therefore probably by him.
SD 8171

119
Two designs for silver châtelaines
41 × 35.5
Inscribed: *The Ermengarde / Eveline Berenger*
Pencil on tracing paper
circa 1900

These are probably by Rex Silver as they are inscribed with working notes in his hand.
SD 8129

120
Design for a silver powder box
37 × 22
Inscribed in Archibald Knox's hand
Bottom of Box / Plan of Lid / ¼ plan of foot / Powder Box
Pencil, watercolour on cartridge paper
circa 1900

This elegant design of birds and flowers is reminiscent of Voysey and is certainly by Archibald Knox.
SD 9267

121
Design for Tudric pewter candlestick
24.5 × 21.5
Inscribed: *Narbyl*
Pencil on tracing paper
circa 1900

This is almost certainly by Archibald Knox and is illustrated in Liberty's *Cymric Silver* catalogue of circa 1900 p68 number 3.
SD 8154

122
Sketch for a silver candlestick
35.5 × 26
Inscribed: *The Thousla* and with working notes in Rex Silver's hand.
Pencil on tracing paper
circa 1900 / 1905

A similar design was exhibited at the Liberty Centenary exhibition held at the Victoria and Albert Museum in 1975 (catalogue number D273). This would seem to be by Rex Silver.
SD 8327

123
Design for a silver bowl
12.5 × 20
Inscribed: *Ostia*
Pencil on tracing paper
circa 1900

This is a typical Archibald Knox design for metalwork and is illustrated in Liberty's *Cymric Silver* catalogue circa 1900, p63 number 3.
SD 8148

124
Design for a sweet basket
37 × 31
Inscribed in Rex Silver's hand: *Sweet Basket / S.7 & The Bollellin / altered*
Pencil on detail paper
circa 1903

A pewter dish was made from this design (see Liberty's catalogue for 1903 p39 number 1). This might well have been designed by Rex Silver as it is annotated in his hand.
SD 8325

125
Design for a pewter bowl
23.5 × 31.5

123

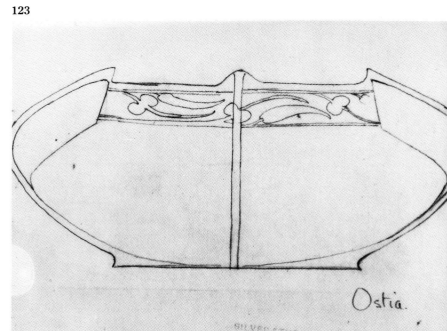

Ostia.

SILVER STUDIO COLL.

126

4 Legs used.

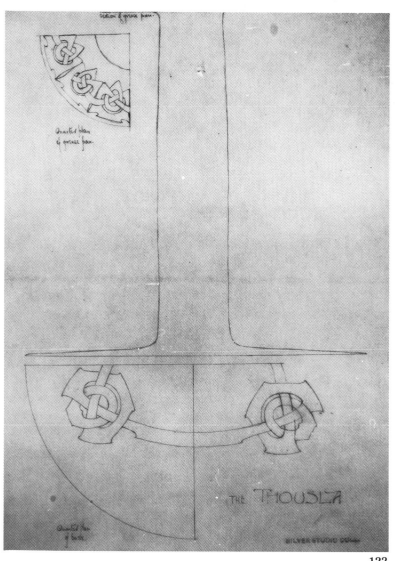

THE THOUSER

SILVER STUDIO COLL.

124

122

131

Inscribed: *05024*
Watercolour, white pastel and pencil on
green cartridge paper
circa 1905

Almost certainly by Harry Silver. A
simple bowl design with a pattern of
small simplified leaves as a border below
the rim and four upright single stems of
rose buds.
SD 1612.

126
Sheet of designs for sweet dish, beaker
and two flower vases all in pewter
33.6 × 37.7
Inscribed by Harry Silver's hand: *Plan /
4 legs used / 2 handles used*
1908

These are all by Harry Silver for Liberty
& Co Ltd. The lower left-hand vase is
illustrated in Liberty's *Yule Tide Gifts*
catalogue for 1910, p120. Note how
Harry Silver is using a neo-Adam style
instead of Arts and Crafts designs.
SD 1643

127
Silver clock
15 × 9.7
1911

Designed for Liberty & Co by Harry
Silver from Silver Studio design
number 06831.
Lent by Mrs William Haxworth

128
Christening set
Length of spoon 15
Spoon and Fork stamped with
Birmingham Hallmark for 1912 and *5790*
Napkin ring stamped *L & Co* and
engraved *Gay*
1912

Designed by Harry Silver for Liberty &
Co and given to his daughter, Gay, as a
christening present.
Lent by Mrs Herman Silver

129
Design for a wallpaper
65 × 64

Inscribed: *2390*
Gouache on cartridge paper
1898

Centre group of five poppies in ogee
panel formed of acanthus leaves. In pale
terracotta, greens, grey/blue on deep
blue ground.
SD3514

130
Four sketches for a wallpaper design
each 20 × 15
Inscribed: *2348 / 2350*
Pencil, watercolour on cartridge paper
1898

These were all for the designs which
were sold to Wylie & Lochead. Note the
opulent combination of poppies and
acanthus scrolls, very typical of Silver
Studio Art Nouveau.
SD 5839, 5838, 5837, 5836

131
Sketch for a wallpaper frieze design
35 × 22.5
Inscribed: *2404*
Pencil, watercolour on cartridge paper
1898

Wallpaper frieze design for the Glasgow
firm, Wylie & Lochead. Roccoco scrolls
and sprays of flowers. In shades of blue,
orange, brown etc on mid-green ground.
SD 5832

132
Design for a wallpaper
47 × 48
Inscribed: *2318*
Gouache on cartridge paper
1898

Very stylised design of chrysanthemum
flowers and leaves in sage and light
green, light blue and on a dark blue
ground.
SD 3544

133
Design for a wallpaper
63 × 83.5
Inscribed: *2464*
Gouache and pencil on cartridge paper
1899

This is a very typical lush Silver Studio
Art Nouveau design, possibly by Harry
Napper. Large poppy with wide twisting
leaves. Yellow and venetian red with
dark red background.
SD 8557

134
Design for a printed textile
59.5 × 69.5
Inscribed: *6 colours / No 2075*
Gouache on cartridge paper
1899

Design of large stylised leaves enclosing groups of stylised flowers — daffodils, bluebells and irises. In greens, blues, yellows on deep blue ground. Possibly by John Illingworth Kay.
SD 3527

135
Design for a wallpaper
79.5 × 66.5
Inscribed: *2452*
Gouache on cartridge paper
1899

Design of vertical curving sprays of bluebells and acanthus in shades of light and dark blue.
SD 3578

136
Design for textile
72 × 59
Inscribed: *No 2072*
Pencil, gouache on cartridge paper
1899

Design of lily flower shaped panels formed from simplified leaves and containing three sprays of flower heads. In terracotta, pink and mid-blue on deep blue ground.
SD 8440

137
Design for a wallpaper
85.5 × 63
Inscribed: *2469*
Gouache on cartridge paper
1899

This design clearly shows the continuing importance of Japan as an influence on Silver Studio designs. The centre is formed from a large chrysanthemum head surrounded by acanthus leaves. These form an ogee panel which in turn is surrounded by single small chrysanthemum sprays. In light and dark green on deep blue/green ground.
SD 8576

138
Design for a printed textile
66.5 x 60
Inscribed: *No 2184*
Gouache on cartridge paper
1899

Typical Silver Studio Art Nouveau design of sprays of poppy heads and acanthus scrolls. In pink and pea green on a venetian red ground.
SD 3565

139
Design for a textile
72 × 55
Inscribed: *2068*

Pencil, gouache on cartridge paper
1899

Printed chintz design of sprays of stylised flowers and leaves arranged in vertical lines. Colours are predominantly yellow and green on a dark blue ground.
SD 8457

140
Wallpaper catalogue
25 × 19
Inscribed: *Jeffrey & Co / The Wallpaper Gallery / 31 Mortimer St., W*
circa 1900

Jeffrey & Co were one of the best wallpaper manufacturers of the day and the Silver Studio regularly supplied them with designs. There are a number of Silver Studio papers in this catalogue, including *The Cotswold* designed by Harry Napper.

141, 142, 143
Three woven furnishing textiles
Various sizes
circa 1900—1905

These textiles were all woven in north-eastern France by Leborgne & Vanoutryve. These are typical of the designs sold by the Silver Studio to this part of France and reveal the importance of their Art Nouveau style on the Continent.

144
The poppy wallpaper frieze
53 × 51
Inscribed: *36070 / 36d per yard*
Stencil and block printed in distemper
circa 1900

Lush typical Silver Studio Art Nouveau pattern of heavy poppy flowers. Printed by Shand Kydd who were famous for their beautifully printed wallpapers.
SW 736

145
Design for a printed textile
61 × 68.5
Inscribed: *No 2181*
Gouache on cartridge paper
circa 1900

Harry Silver was particularly good at designs that were in the tradition of William Morris. This is a typical example based on poppies and leaves. Pinks, greens, ochre on deep blue ground.
SD 8521

146
Design for a wallpaper
68 × 47
Inscribed: *No 2688*

Gouache and pencil on cartridge paper
circa 1900

This design might well be by Archibald Knox. The motifs of stylised roses resemble closely those used by him on metalwork designs. In pinks and greens on green ground.
SD 8548

147
Design for a wallpaper
69.3 × 91
Inscribed: *No 2252*
Gouache on cartridge paper
circa 1900

Design of daisies and camomile flowers in naturalistic sprays on clear ground. In yellows and green on white background.
SD 1409

148
Design for a printed textile
54.5 × 74
Inscribed: *975*
Charcoal, gouache on detail paper
circa 1900

This design is almost certainly by Harry Napper. It is very stylised with flattened, sharply delineated flowers and leaves. The upper right hand corner is coloured in gouache in tertiary shades.
SD 1226

149
Design for a wallpaper frieze
58 × 48
Inscribed: *Eton Planted / 03724*
Charcoal, coloured pencil and gouache on detail paper
circa 1900

Elegant Arts and Crafts design by Harry Silver of tulips, topiary hedge and trees.
SD 710

150
Woven silk and cotton doublecloth
60 × 30
circa 1900

This was probably woven by Alexander Morton from a design by John Illingworth Kay of stylised trees and shrubs in gold, red and blue.
ST 12

151
Furniture catalogue
22 × 15
Inscribed: *An Officer's Ideal Quarters*
1901

Most of the furniture, metalwork, wallpapers and stencils used in the illustrations of this Norman & Stacey

139

142

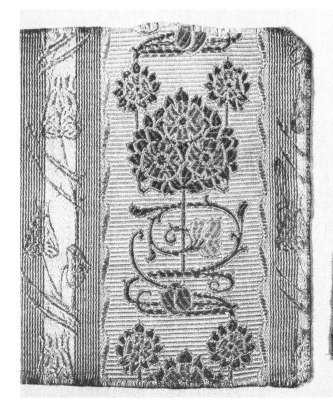

141

catalogue were by Harry Napper, and it provides a marvellous record of his talent for designing for a wide range of objects in the Art Nouveau style. (The style of these interiors would be described by contemporary writers as 'quaint').
SE 480

152
Design for a printed textile
65 × 61
Inscribed: *No 2179*
Gouache on cartridge paper
1901

Design of ogee panels formed from stylised flowers and acanthus leaves. The panels contain chrysanthemum heads. In pinks, purples, greens on dark blue ground.
SD 3537

153
Design for a printed textile
73.5 × 61.5
Inscribed: *No 2459*
Gouache on cartridge paper
1902

This is a typical Harry Napper design of groups of three stylised poppy flowers on one stem with an Art Nouveau whiplash curve. In blues and yellow/ochre.
SD 3524

154
Design for a wallpaper frieze
61.5 × 89
Inscribed: *03329*
Pastel on detail paper
1902

This design was probably by Harry Silver, who produced some of the best Silver Studio Arts and Crafts designs. Trees, birds and deer on a light ground.
SD 1424

155
The Venetian wallpaper frieze
56 × 188
Inscribed *(verso): Venetian Frieze /2yd pattern / B3381*
Block printed distemper on paper
1902

Although not by the Silver Studio, this frieze has been included as an example of the rather mysterious and exotic style of decoration that went hand-in-hand with Art Nouveau. The Venetian Frieze was designed by George Fisher Jones and was supplied almost without a repeat.
SW 648

156
Wallpaper — *Flaming Tulips*
Distemper on wallpaper
1903

This delightful wallpaper is typical of the best of Wylie & Lochead wallpaper. It was designed in 1903 by a close friend of the Silvers — Arthur Gwatkin, and it is of stylised tulips and leaves. The colours are red, fawn, ochre on cream ground.
SW 60

157
Design for a wallpaper
71 × 61.5
Inscribed: *No 2561*
Watercolour on cartridge paper
1904

This design is probably by Harry Napper and consists of parallel curving lines formed from poppy flowers and acanthus leaves in blues and greens.
SD 3540

158
Liberty catalogue
18 × 25
Inscribed: *Yule-Tide Gifts / 1904—1905*
1904

This catalogue includes several examples of metalwork and textiles from Silver Studio Art Nouveau designs.
SE 1087

159
Design for a woven textile
32 × 27.5
Inscribed: *04937*
Pencil, coloured pencil and gouache on detail paper
circa 1905

A charming late Art Nouveau design, possibly by Harry Silver, of small stylised roses and stem forming a vertical stripe.
SD 732

160
Catalogue of fireplaces and overmantels
27.5 × 21.5
Inscribed on cover: *WN Froy & Sons / 66 King Street, Hammersmith. Wood Fireplaces. Overmantels*
1905

Often one of the most striking pieces of Art Nouveau in the ordinary middle-class English house was to be seen in the fireplace. This is a catalogue of typical designs of the period.
SE 1067

161
Design for a printed textile
72.5 × 50.5
Inscribed: *32665*
Gouache and pencil on cartridge paper
1905

This is probably by Harry Silver, although there is a distinct hint of Harry Napper's work. Very striking design of single flowers enclosed by curving green leaves forming ogee panels. Greens, ochre, cream on dark blue ground.
SD 8555

162
Design for a wallpaper frieze
55.5 × 85.5
Inscribed: *04102*
Charcoal, watercolour and coloured pencil on detail paper
circa 1905

Delightful, simple Arts and Crafts design, probably by Harry Silver, of leaping rabbits with trees at either end of the panel and a background of hills. The design is coloured in pale blue and purple crayon with one panel (centre right) coloured in watercolour.
SD 1423

163
Wallpaper sample
62 × 57
Distemper on wallpaper
circa 1905

This paper bears a distinct resemblance to CFA Voysey's *The Squire's Garden* paper of 1898. This was probably made by John Lines from a design by Harry Silver and is typical of the Arts and Crafts designs produced by the Studio at this time.
SW 657

164
Design for a printed textile
62.5 × 74.5
Inscribed: *No 32309*
Gouache on cartridge paper
1906

Very stylish Art Nouveau design of large, light blue poppy heads.
SD 3530

165
Design for a printed textile
62.5 × 46
Inscribed: *No 32380*
Gouache on cartridge paper
1906

Design of stylised flowers and leaves arranged in vertical lines. In blues and greens on dark grey/blue ground.
SD 3604

166
Design for a printed textile
67.5 x 62
Inscribed: *No 32266 / H*
Gouache on cartridge paper
1906

This design shows the continuing popularity of William Morris designs in the early 1900s. Large stylised roses and acanthus leaves resembling Morris designs of the 1870s. In terracotta, pink, ochre on grey/blue ground.
SD 3528

167
Design for a printed textile
69.5 × 57.5
Inscribed: *32242*
Gouache on cartridge paper
1906

Morris influenced design of upwardly spiralling stylised buttercups in pinks, ochres and greens on dark green ground.

Probably by Harry Silver.
SD 3526

168
Wallpaper catalogue
16.5 × 18.5
Inscribed on cover: *The JL & S Studies in Harmony Wallpapers / John Line & Sons Ltd / Tottenham Court Road, W*
1908

This catalogue contains illustrations of wallpapers from the Silver Studio. John Line was a friend of Arthur Silver and one of his earliest and best customers. As a result, the Silver Studio supplied John Line with wallpaper designs until the late 1950s.
SE 117

169
Wallpaper catalogue
24.5 × 18.5
Inscribed: *Shand Kydd / Wallpapers 1909 / London NW*
1909

This catalogue has been included to show illustrated examples of stylish late Art Nouveau papers used in suggested interiors.
SE 1110

170
Design for a printed textile
23.5 × 16.5
Inscribed: *33173 / 06633*
Pencil, watercolour on detail paper
1909

170

This is a design by Herbert Crofts who became head designer at the Silver Studio after World War I. It was sold to Koechlin Baumgarten as a dress print, and is typical of the reproduction historic styles that succeeded Art Nouveau as the Silver Studio's major design style.
SD 9268

171
Linoleum catalogue
15 × 19.5
Inscribed on cover: *Staines Inlaid Linoleum / A remarkable floor covering*
circa 1910

The Silver Studio produced Art Nouveau designs for a very wide range of

materials. Shown here are examples of their designs used for linoleum.
SD 1272

172
Design for a printed textile
24.5 × 19.5
Inscribed: *06651 / 33227*
Pencil, watercolour on detail paper
1910

Another traditional design by Herbert Crofts. Art Nouveau had become an out-of-date style in Britain by 1910, and traditional brocade patterns, all scrolls and flowers, became the popular middle-class furnishing style.
SD 9269

173
Three designs for dress silks
each 16 × 13
Each inscribed with a Silver Studio design number: *32968 / 1864A /32970*
Pencil, watercolour on cartridge paper
1910

These three designs are probably the work of Harry Silver. The left and centre designs are of single sprays of conventionlised flowers. The design on the right is rather more elaborately Art Nouveau with flattened, stylised flowers and curving stems. All are in the pale mauve/blue/green colours much favoured for dress silks at the beginning of the 20th century.
SD 733, SD 734, SD 735

172